D0274794

Slimming World mediterranean *magic*

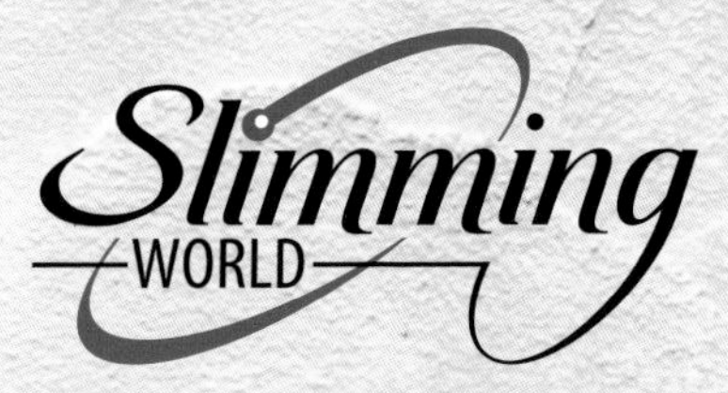

touching hearts, changing lives

a gloriously sunny Slimming World *welcome to* mediterranean *magic...*

...a recipe book that's bursting with all the colour, warmth and passion of Mediterranean food!

Mealtimes in the Med are special times. They're about sitting down together with family and friends, and enjoying the best things in life together. The dishes are rich, bursting with flavour and tradition, and infused with love – the perfect combination for us because, just like our friends in the Mediterranean, we love, love, love food!

And that's the basis upon which I founded Food Optimising back in 1969 – for the love of food. Probably like you, I'd tried every diet under the sun, without lasting success. Hunger, deprivation and guilt were NOT the answer. No diet that made me skip meals, cut out my favourite foods, eat separately from my family or ruin my social life was ever going to work for me! It certainly wouldn't work in the Mediterranean! And I'm sure you also realise it's a non-starter when it comes to lasting weight-loss success. What we all need is a flexible way of eating – one that liberates us from the hunger and the stress of obsessive calorie-counting.

Sounds positively magical? Well, I agree – it is! The whole Slimming World package of Food Optimising and IMAGE Therapy (which stands for Individual Motivation And Group Experience) replaces that destructive cycle with a combination of unlimited (no counting), filling (no hunger) and healthy foods, making losing weight easier than you could ever believe. Add to that our unique group support system (which makes success five times more likely than going it alone) and it's game, set and match! When you're in a Slimming World group, it's one of the safest, most compassionate, understanding, helpful and fun places to be for anyone wanting to achieve their weight loss dreams.

Since 1969 we've been working with top scientists, psychologists and the greatest experts of all – slimmers – to develop an eating plan that allows people to fill up on unlimited quantities of delicious everyday foods and still lose weight. Bonkers, right? Impossible? The evidence is overwhelmingly otherwise.

New research in the *British Journal of General Practice shows* that over 12 months, Slimming World members lose more weight than members of other weight loss clubs. That's because Food Optimising is based on a deep understanding of how our appetite – both physical and psychological – works and how we can satisfy it without gaining weight. Vitally, through the powerful work that Slimming World Consultants do in our groups, we also know how to inspire and motivate slimmers every step of the way on their journey towards their own personal target weight.

That genuine care and understanding is what makes Slimming World groups so special. It's why we now have around 12,000 groups in the UK and Ireland – every one run by highly trained, compassionate Consultants who, as former members, have experienced the warmth, love and success of Slimming World for themselves. And it's why we offer the very best support and inspiration there is for slimmers, everywhere and anywhere.

This wonderful book is just a small (but perfectly formed!) part of that support and inspiration. Whether you've already discovered Slimming World and you're motoring towards your goal, or you're dipping your toe into the water before you dive in, *Mediterranean Magic* will give you a taste of your gorgeous, slim and happy future. A future that's full of flavour, bubbling with fun and made for sharing with family and friends.

So come with us on this magical Mediterranean journey and fill your home with sunshine every single day. It's a marvellous way to make new, thrilling, life-changing habits. Together, Slimming World and you, we really can make dreams come true.

Oceans of love and warmest sunshine wishes, as always,

Margaret Miles-Bramwell

Margaret Miles-Bramwell OBE HonMUniv FRSA
Founder and Chairman

come on a journey around the Med... *...with* Slimming World

Vive la Food Optimising!

If you've already flicked through the pages of *Mediterranean Magic* you might have noticed something a little confusing. If this is a slimming cookbook, where's all the diet food? The truth is, at Slimming World, there's no such thing as diet food! Instead, our eating plan is based on delicious, everyday ingredients made into hearty, satisfying, mouth-watering meals – meals you eat in portions to suit your appetite. No obsessive weighing, measuring or counting. No deprivation, hunger or guilt. Welcome to the revolution. Welcome to Food Optimising.

Weight loss that lasts a lifetime

Food Optimising is based on the sound scientific principle that to lose weight you have to take in less energy (in the form of calories) than you use. That part of the equation is simple. The stroke of genius behind the plan – the reason why Slimming World is light years ahead of any other weight loss programme – lies in our unique approach to weight loss. And that approach is grounded in the concept of Free Foods.

Free Foods sweep away all the fear of hunger, worry about over-eating and the stress of counting, weighing and measuring that are the downfall of so many slimmers. These 'magical' foods include lean meat, poultry and fish, as well as eggs, potatoes, pasta, rice, pulses, fat free dairy products, fruits and vegetables. Free Foods are super-filling, super-satisfying and inexpensive – plus they couldn't be simpler to shop for, prepare and cook. Best of all, they're absolutely unlimited. Any time, any amount, any place – the only limit is your appetite!

By basing meals on the huge range of Free Foods, Food Optimisers naturally reduce their energy intake without feeling deprived or counting a single calorie – resulting in week after week of delicious meals, and steady weight loss that feels almost effortless.

Filling power is slimming power!

Following many years of independent research – much of which Slimming World has supported and contributed to – there's now robust scientific evidence which proves

With Food Optimising you can enjoy cracking losses on the scales each week – all with just a few changes to the way you shop for and cook your meals.

that eating plenty of protein-rich foods is the very best way to satisfy your appetite and stay fuller for longer. And that's great news for Food Optimisers, because many Free Foods tick that box beautifully – from lean meat, poultry and fish to eggs, beans, tofu and fat-free dairy products. We call them P foods (because they're Protein-rich). Following very closely behind protein in the satiety stakes is carbohydrate – which is why our long list of Free Foods also includes comforting staples like pasta, rice and potatoes. At Slimming World, we encourage members to fill their plates with these super-satisfying Free Foods and, where they can, to make up at least a third of that plate with what we call 'Speed' (or S) foods – fruits and vegetables that are bulky and filling but also super-low in calories. It's this principle that gives our members the healthiest, most balanced, most satisfying route to target; a natural, simple and sustainable way of eating that sticks – for life!

A perfect balance

As well as Free Foods, Food Optimising has two other key elements: Healthy Extras and Syns. Healthy Extras are foods rich in nutrients, such as calcium or dietary fibre, which are important for weight loss and overall health. Each day, Food Optimisers choose two servings of Healthy Extra foods such as wholemeal bread, nuts and seeds, cereal, cheese or milk – perfect for eating with or in between meals, for even greater choice and flexibility.

And what about Syns? Syns are the food choices (yes, even more food!) that help to make Food Optimising so enjoyable and easy to stick to. Each day, Slimming World members can choose how to use their allocation of Syns – maybe on a chocolate bar or slice of cake, a creamy sauce with dinner, mayonnaise in a sandwich or a glass of wine. Foods and drinks that have a 'Syn value' tend to be high in calories for their weight – so they're very easy to over-eat. Totting up the Syns you enjoy each day helps you to protect your weight loss without missing out on your favourite things – because life's for living!

Together, the synergy of Free Foods, Healthy Extras and Syns is an unbeatable combination that makes Food Optimising the most flexible, generous and enjoyable weight loss plan you'll find.

And how about those weeks when you really want to power up your weight loss – perhaps as you approach your target weight, or before (or after!) a special occasion or holiday? No, we still won't expect you to go even the slightest bit hungry – or miss out on your favourite treats! Instead, we ask you to add a touch more structure to your eating and change the make-up of your meals slightly, filling your plate with those super-slimming S and P foods. It's simple, it's effective – and we call it Extra Easy SP. Follow this plan and you'll love the results on the scales just as much as you'll love the food!

No weighing,
no measuring,
no counting…
no kidding!

La dolce vita!

One aspect of Slimming World that often surprises new members is that it fits so beautifully with everyone's lifestyle – whether you're following a special diet for health or religious reasons, are vegan or vegetarian, or have strong food likes and dislikes.

So whether you love a hearty veggie pasta bake, crispy chips, a mixed grill or curry 'n' rice, with Food Optimising you can go right ahead and still enjoy cracking losses on the scales each week – all with just a few changes to the way you shop for and cook your meals.

Boredom is banned!

At Slimming World, food isn't the enemy. We love the stuff! And we encourage our members to be as passionate about eating as they've ever been – the Food Optimising way! Our community of Consultants, staff and members are constantly sharing ideas, recipes, photos and how-to videos – in group each week, across social media, on LifelineOnline (our website exclusively for members), in our gorgeous glossy magazine and inspiring recipe books just like this one! There's so much choice and variety, you'll never be bored!

Where the magic happens

This collection of 'bellissimo' recipes gives you just a taste of the Slimming World experience. The real magic happens when you experience the world's most flexible, filling and liberating eating plan alongside IMAGE Therapy – and you can only get that in a Slimming World group.

IMAGE Therapy stands for Individual Motivation And Group Experience – and it's why more people in the UK choose to go to Slimming World every week than any other weight loss group. Developed over 45 years, this unique group support system is led by our caring, highly trained Consultants, and allows members to share ideas, insights, problems, recipes and milestones – in a setting that's completely supportive, inspiring and non-judgemental.

IMAGE Therapy is fun, informative, inspiring and often life-changing, helping members to steer their way past obstacles and plot their path to success.

In fact, the safety, warmth and compassion of IMAGE Therapy is the beating heart of every Slimming World group – and many members tell us that it's not just their favourite part of the Slimming World group but also the highlight of their week!

At Slimming World, food isn't the enemy – we love the stuff!

Keep on moving

Together with Food Optimising and IMAGE Therapy, the third element that makes the Slimming World experience so special is Body Magic. This unique lifestyle-based activity programme isn't about pushing yourself to the limits, getting up at 4am to go to the gym or running marathons (unless you want to!). Body Magic is the wonderful synergy you create when you're Food Optimising while building some regular moderate activity into your everyday life – whether that's walking the dog, gardening, playing tag with the kids or cycling to work. Just like our eating plan, it's sustainable and it's fun – and we'll praise and reward you for your achievements at every stage of your journey. No fads, no boredom, no dead ends.

So there it is. Food Optimising, IMAGE Therapy and Body Magic – an unrivalled recipe for slimming success that has helped millions of men and women lose weight and find health and happiness. If you'd love to become one of them, we're here for you in groups the length and breadth of the UK and Ireland. Enjoy creating (and eating!) the delicious dishes here in *Mediterranean Magic* – we hope they inspire you as you set out on the journey to your dream you.

For details of a warm and friendly group near you, call 0844 897 8000 or visit www.slimmingworld.com

France

Our neighbours over the Channel are world-famous for their food, and the good news is you don't need a Michelin star to cook France's simplest and most satisfying dishes! Choose from irresistible rustic stews, sensational salads and elegant yet easy-peasy puds.

onion soup

serves 4

Free

❄ Ⓥ SP

ready in 1 hour

low calorie cooking spray

5 onions, thinly sliced

3 garlic cloves, thinly sliced

850ml vegetable stock or water

4 tbsp balsamic vinegar

salt and freshly ground black pepper

small handful of finely chopped fresh thyme leaves

Slow-cooking the onions really brings out their sweetness in this heart-warming soup and balsamic vinegar adds a delicious savoury richness.

Spray a wide, heavy-based saucepan with low calorie cooking spray and place over a low heat. Add the onions and garlic and sauté for 40 minutes or until browned, stirring occasionally.

Add the stock or water and the balsamic vinegar and bring to the boil. Turn the heat to low and simmer for about 10 minutes.

Season to taste, divide between bowls and scatter over the thyme.

For an indulgent and very authentic twist, add some cheesy croutons to your soup. Make a slice of cheese on toast using 15g of Gruyère and a slice of wholemeal bread from a small 400g loaf. Cut it into eight pieces and divide between the bowls to serve, adding 1½ Syns per serving.

soupe au pistou

serves 4

1 Syn per serving

ready in 35 minutes

Pistou is the French take on Italian pesto and this intensely garlicky sauce adds depth to a filling soup packed with fresh vegetables.

low calorie cooking spray

1 onion, finely chopped

2 garlic cloves, finely chopped

2 celery sticks, roughly chopped

2 carrots, peeled and diced

2 potatoes, peeled and diced

1 ready-made bouquet garni

1.75 litres boiling vegetable stock

200g dried vermicelli pasta, broken into small pieces

salt and freshly ground black pepper

100g trimmed green beans, cut into pieces

400g can cannellini or haricot beans, drained and rinsed

for the pistou

50g fresh basil

4 garlic cloves, finely chopped

4 level tbsp freshly grated Parmesan

100ml vegetable stock, cooled

Spray a wide, heavy-based pan with low calorie cooking spray and place over a medium heat. Add the onion, garlic, celery, carrots and potatoes and fry for 3-4 minutes, until slightly coloured. Add the bouquet garni.

Add the stock and vermicelli and season to taste. Cover, bring the soup to a simmer and cook for 10 minutes. Add the green beans and cannellini or haricot beans and cook for another 5 minutes or until the veg and vermicelli are just tender.

Meanwhile, put all the pistou ingredients in a mixing bowl, season and blend using a stick blender – it should be bright green and have a fairly smooth consistency.

Remove and discard the bouquet garni, ladle the soup into bowls and swirl a quarter of the pistou into each bowl to serve.

moules marinières

serves 4

½ **Syn** per serving

ready in 15 minutes

2kg live mussels

6 garlic cloves, finely chopped

1 onion, finely chopped

1 bay leaf

1 tbsp fennel seeds, crushed

4 tbsp dry white wine

400ml boiling fish stock

100g fat free natural fromage frais

small handful of finely chopped fresh dill, plus a few sprigs to garnish

salt and freshly ground black pepper

lemon wedges, to serve

Mussels are so cheap to buy and this stunning starter tastes as amazing as it looks. You can eat the mussels with your fingers and use a spoon to scoop up all the herby, winey juices.

Scrub the mussels, pulling off any beards, and discard any that are damaged or are open and don't close when tapped against the sink.

Put the mussels, garlic, onion, bay leaf, fennel seeds, wine and stock in a large pan and place over a high heat. Cover tightly and boil for 5-6 minutes, shaking the pan frequently, until all the mussels have opened (discard any that remain closed).

Drain, reserving the cooking liquid, and divide the mussels between four bowls.

Whisk the fromage frais into the reserved cooking liquid and pour it over the mussels. Scatter over the chopped dill and dill sprigs, season and serve with lemon wedges to squeeze over.

beef bourguignon

serves 4

1½ Syns per serving

❄

ready in 2 hours 20 minutes

---

low calorie cooking spray

6 back bacon rashers, visible fat removed, roughly chopped

3 large onions, thinly sliced

700g lean casserole steak, visible fat removed, cut into bite-sized pieces

3 garlic cloves, finely chopped

175ml red wine

400ml boiling beef stock

1 tbsp tomato purée

a sprig of fresh rosemary

a sprig of fresh thyme

1 bay leaf

salt and freshly ground black pepper

1 swede or 2 turnips, peeled and cut into large chunks

This timeless slow-cooked beef casserole is so simple it almost cooks itself – it's a perfect Sunday lunch!

Preheat your oven to 180°C/Fan 160°C/Gas 4.

Spray a large non-stick frying pan with low calorie cooking spray and place over a medium heat. Fry the bacon and onions for 3-4 minutes or until starting to brown then increase the heat to high, add the steak and stir-fry for 6-7 minutes or until nicely browned (this is important for the flavour of the finished dish).

Stir in the garlic, wine, stock, tomato purée, rosemary, thyme and bay leaf. Season, bring to the boil and transfer to a casserole dish. Cover and bake for 2 hours, adding the swede or turnips for the last 30 minutes.

Serve in shallow bowls with salad or your favourite vegetables.

Make this recipe Free by replacing the wine with another 175ml of stock.

steak béarnaise with quick boulangère potatoes

This ever-popular bistro dish gives you an irresistible plate of sizzling steak, creamy sauce and cheesy potatoes for just 1½ Syns! Our easy recipe will save you stacks of Syns and loads of time.

First make the béarnaise sauce. Put the shallots, peppercorns, vinegar, stock and most of the tarragon in a small saucepan over a high heat. Boil for 6-8 minutes or until the liquid has reduced by one-third, taking care not to let it boil dry. Strain the liquid into a heatproof bowl, discarding the flavourings, then leave to cool. Whisk in the mayonnaise and fromage frais, season with a little garlic salt and keep it at room temperature until you're ready to serve.

Preheat your grill to medium-high.

To make the potatoes, pour the stock into a large pan and bring to the boil. Add the potatoes and onions and simmer for 10-12 minutes or until just tender. Drain well.

Spray a shallow baking dish with low calorie cooking spray. Arrange the potato mixture in the dish, season with garlic salt and black pepper and sprinkle over the Parmesan, then spray again with low calorie cooking spray. Grill for 3-4 minutes or until nicely browned and keep warm.

Meanwhile, season the steaks on both sides and spray with low calorie cooking spray. Place a large non-stick griddle pan over a high heat (if you don't have a griddle, a frying pan is fine). When it's smoking hot, cook the steaks to your liking (2 minutes each side for rare, 3 minutes each side for medium or 4 minutes each side for well done). Drain on kitchen paper and rest for a few minutes.

Cook the spinach in a little boiling water for 2-3 minutes or until just wilted then squeeze out any excess water in a sieve and season to taste.

Divide the potatoes and spinach between warmed plates and top with the steaks. Spoon the béarnaise sauce over the steaks and scatter over the remaining tarragon to serve.

serves 4

1½ Syns per serving

ready in 45 minutes

---

4 lean beef fillet steaks, visible fat removed

400g baby spinach leaves

for the béarnaise sauce

2 shallots, finely chopped

10 black peppercorns

1 tbsp white wine vinegar

150ml boiling vegetable stock

small handful of finely chopped fresh tarragon

2 level tbsp extra-light mayonnaise

100g fat free natural fromage frais

garlic salt, to taste

for the boulangère potatoes

1 litre vegetable stock

1kg floury potatoes, such as King Edward, peeled and cut into thin batons

3 large onions, thinly sliced

low calorie cooking spray

2 tsp garlic salt

salt and freshly ground black pepper

4 level tbsp freshly grated Parmesan

beef daube

serves 4

Free

❄

ready in 2 hours 20 minutes

---

low calorie cooking spray

700g lean casserole steak, visible fat removed, cut into bite-sized pieces

2 garlic cloves, crushed

2 onions, roughly chopped

3 carrots, roughly chopped

2 turnips, peeled and roughly chopped

600ml boiling beef stock

salt and freshly ground black pepper

2 tsp dried mixed herbs

This hearty, warming stew of beef and chunky vegetables is the ideal dinner on a cold winter's night!

Preheat the oven to 160°C/Fan 140°C/Gas 3.

Spray a large non-stick frying pan with low calorie cooking spray and place over a medium heat. Add the meat and fry until browned on all sides.

Transfer the meat to an ovenproof casserole dish along with the garlic, onions, carrots, turnips and stock. Season to taste and add the dried herbs. Cover tightly and cook in the oven for 2 hours.

Serve hot with your favourite potatoes and vegetables.

ham and herb omelette with french fries

serves 4

Free

ready in 30 minutes

12 large eggs*

small handful of finely chopped fresh chives

small handful of finely chopped fresh tarragon

small handful of finely chopped fresh parsley

half a bunch of finely chopped spring onions

8 slices of lean ham, visible fat removed, finely chopped

for the French fries

6 large potatoes, peeled and cut into fries

low calorie cooking spray

salt and freshly ground black pepper

**Pregnant women, the elderly and babies are advised not to eat raw or partially cooked eggs.*

The French think of the omelette as the classic test of a chef's skills. Our recipe makes it easy for everyone from the beginner to the experienced home cook!

Preheat the oven to 200°C/Fan 180°C/Gas 6.

First make the French fries. Cook the fries in a saucepan of lightly salted boiling water over a high heat for 5-6 minutes. Drain well and spread out the fries on two baking sheets lined with non-stick baking parchment. Spray with low calorie cooking spray and bake for 12-15 minutes or until golden and crisp. Season with salt.

Meanwhile, crack the eggs into a measuring jug or large bowl and whisk lightly. Add the herbs and spring onions and season to taste.

Spray a medium-sized non-stick frying pan with low calorie cooking spray and place over a medium-high heat. Add one-quarter of the egg mixture and gently shake the pan to distribute the egg evenly. Cook for 20 seconds or so until it begins to bubble, then draw the edges into the centre with a wooden spoon and shake the pan again to redistribute the uncooked egg. Scatter over one-quarter of the ham. The omelette is ready when the base is set and it is still slightly runny in the middle. (If you prefer, you can cook it until completely set.)

Remove the pan from the heat and fold the omelette over. Turn out on to a plate, wrap in tin foil and keep warm while you make three more omelettes.

Serve the omelettes hot with French fries and salad.

If you have two frying pans, you can speed things up by cooking two omelettes at the same time.

sausage cassoulet

serves 4

3 Syns per serving

❄

ready in 50 minutes

---

8 Sainsbury's Be Good to Yourself Cumberland Sausages, Less Than 3% Fat*

low calorie cooking spray

1 onion, thinly sliced

2 carrots, peeled and roughly chopped

½ tsp dried red chilli flakes

2 garlic cloves, finely chopped

400g can chopped tomatoes

500ml boiling vegetable stock

1 bay leaf

a few sprigs of fresh thyme

1 tsp dried herbes de Provence

100ml red wine

2 sweet potatoes, peeled and roughly chopped

400g can haricot beans, drained and rinsed

2 leeks, thickly sliced

salt and freshly ground black pepper

small handful of roughly chopped fresh parsley, to garnish

**We've counted 1 Syn each for the sausages but Syn values for branded foods can change. You can find the very latest information online at www.slimmingworld.com/lifelineonline.*

This spectacular stew is packed with juicy sausages and filling veg with a warming hint of chilli – everyone will be asking for an encore!

Cook the sausages according to the packet instructions and transfer to a plate.

Meanwhile, spray a large non-stick frying pan with low calorie cooking spray and place over a medium-low heat. Fry the onion and carrots for 10 minutes, stirring often, then stir in the chilli flakes and garlic and cook for 1 minute.

Add the tomatoes, stock, bay leaf, thyme, dried herbs and red wine and stir. Turn the heat to high and bring to the boil, then reduce the heat to medium-low and simmer for 10 minutes.

Cut the sausages in half diagonally and add to the pan. Add the sweet potatoes and cook for 10 minutes, stirring occasionally, then add the beans and leeks and cook for a further 10 minutes. Season to taste, scatter over the parsley and serve hot.

coq au vin
with herby mash

This wonderful combination of chicken, vegetables and wine is a rustic delight. Serve it with a big pile of mash to mop up all the juices.

serves 4

2 Syns per serving

ready in 1 hour

---

low calorie cooking spray

4 skinless chicken legs, visible fat removed

12 back bacon rashers, visible fat removed, roughly chopped

10 shallots, peeled and trimmed

1 bay leaf

400g baby carrots, scrubbed and trimmed

4 garlic cloves, finely chopped

400g button mushrooms, halved

1 level tbsp chicken gravy granules

750ml boiling chicken stock

100ml red wine

salt and freshly ground black pepper

200g mangetout

for the herby mash

1kg floury potatoes, such as King Edward, peeled and roughly chopped

150ml boiling vegetable stock

large handful of finely chopped mixed fresh herbs such as parsley, tarragon, chives and dill

Spray a large ovenproof casserole pan with low calorie cooking spray and place over a high heat. Add the chicken legs and cook for 4-5 minutes, turning often, until lightly browned all over.

Add the bacon, shallots, bay leaf, carrots, garlic, mushrooms, gravy granules, stock and wine. Season, stir and bring to the boil. Turn the heat to medium-low, cover and simmer for 30 minutes or until the chicken is cooked through, adding the mangetout for the last 10 minutes.

Meanwhile, cook the potatoes in a saucepan of lightly salted boiling water for 12-15 minutes or until tender. Drain, return to the pan and mash with the stock. Stir in the herbs, season and keep warm.

Serve hot with a good grind of pepper and a big dollop of herby mash.

duck a l'orange

serves 4

½ **Syn** per serving

ready in 35 minutes

---

4 duck breasts, skinned and visible fat removed

salt and freshly ground black pepper

low calorie cooking spray

2 garlic cloves, crushed

½ Savoy cabbage, shredded

for the sauce

2 tsp sweetener

4 tbsp white wine vinegar

finely grated zest and juice of 1 orange

350ml boiling chicken stock

In this classic partnership, the richness of the duck goes brilliantly with the zesty orange sauce.

First make the sauce. Put the sweetener and vinegar into a saucepan, bring to the boil over a high heat and reduce until it begins to caramelise. Add the orange juice and keep cooking until reduced by two-thirds. Add the chicken stock, turn the heat to low and simmer for 15-20 minutes. Add half of the orange zest and simmer for another 2-3 minutes, then remove from the heat and keep warm.

Meanwhile, preheat the oven to 200°C/Fan 180°C/Gas 6.

Using a sharp knife, score a diamond pattern into the skinned side of each duck breast and season to taste.

Place a non-stick frying pan over a high heat, spray with low calorie cooking spray and add the duck breasts, skinned side down. Cook until lightly browned – about 7-8 minutes – then turn and cook for a further 30 seconds. Transfer to the oven and cook for 5 minutes. Remove from the oven and leave to rest, skinned side up.

While the duck is in the oven, wipe the pan you used for the duck with kitchen paper. Spray with low calorie cooking spray and turn the heat to medium-high. Add the garlic and cabbage and stir-fry for 4-5 minutes. Season to taste and keep warm.

Slice the duck breasts and divide between warmed plates. Pour the sauce over the duck, sprinkle with the remaining zest and serve with the cabbage and your favourite potatoes.

bouillabaisse

serves 4

1 Syn per serving

ready in 40 minutes

200g live mussels (optional)

750g potatoes, peeled and cut into bite-sized chunks

low calorie cooking spray

2 leeks, white parts only, finely diced

4 garlic cloves, thinly sliced

2 tsp fennel seeds

½ tsp dried red chilli flakes

4 tomatoes, roughly chopped

2 tbsp tomato purée

1.5 litres boiling fish stock

1 ready-made bouquet garni

300g white fish fillet, cut into chunks

300g salmon fillet, cut into chunks

200g raw peeled king or tiger prawns, with or without tails

salt and freshly ground black pepper

small handful of finely chopped dill, to garnish

for the rouille

4 tbsp extra-light mayonnaise

1 garlic clove, crushed

1 tsp cayenne pepper

pinch of saffron threads (optional)

This vibrant dish from Marseille was traditionally made by local fishermen using the fish they couldn't sell such as rascasse, a flamboyantly coloured spiny rockfish! We've used easy-to-find seafood instead!

If you're using mussels, scrub them and pull off any beards. Discard any that are damaged or are open and don't close when tapped against the sink. Set aside.

Cook the potatoes in a saucepan of lightly salted boiling water for 12-15 minutes.

Meanwhile, spray a large non-stick saucepan with low calorie cooking spray and place over a medium heat. Add the leeks, garlic, fennel seeds and dried red chilli and stir-fry for 3 minutes.

Add the tomatoes, tomato purée, stock and bouquet garni and bring to the boil. Stir in the white fish and salmon, bring back to the boil, then reduce the heat and simmer gently for 5 minutes or until the fish is cooked through. Add the mussels and prawns to the pan and cook for another 3-4 minutes.

Drain the potatoes and add to the fish, seasoning with salt and freshly ground black pepper.

Meanwhile, make the rouille by mixing the mayonnaise, garlic, cayenne pepper and saffron, if using (saffron is expensive but makes a real difference to the flavour).

Discard any mussels that have not opened and divide the stew between four shallow bowls. Scatter over the dill, add a dollop of rouille to each bowl and serve hot.

Traditionally, fishermen strain off the cooking broth and enjoy it as a starter with the rouille, then eat the fish as a main course. Try it this way if you like!

Cocteau

cod provençal

serves 4

Free

❄

ready in 1 hour 10 minutes

Fresh, flaky cod is always a treat and in this tasty meal it's complemented by plenty of vegetables and filling beans.

- low calorie cooking spray
- 1 large onion, thinly sliced
- 1 fennel bulb, halved and sliced lengthways
- 3 garlic cloves, thinly sliced
- 2 tsp coriander seeds, crushed
- 1 tsp dried mixed herbs
- 1 bay leaf
- finely grated zest of ½ orange
- 2 x 400g cans chopped tomatoes
- 400g can cannellini or flageolet beans, drained and rinsed
- 200g green beans, trimmed and halved
- 2 courgettes, halved and sliced
- salt and freshly ground black pepper
- 4 thick skinless cod fillets, cut into large chunks
- small handful of roughly chopped fresh parsley, to garnish

Spray a large frying pan with low calorie cooking spray and place over a medium heat. Add the onion and cook for 5 minutes or until softened and lightly browned, stirring often. Add the fennel and cook for a further 10 minutes, stirring occasionally. Add the garlic, coriander seeds, mixed herbs, bay leaf and orange zest and cook for 2 minutes more, stirring occasionally.

Add the tomatoes and 750ml of water and bring to a simmer. Reduce the heat to medium-low and cook for 10 minutes, stirring occasionally. Add the beans and courgettes, return to a simmer and cook for 15-20 minutes or until the veg is just tender. Season to taste.

Add the cod to the pan, cover and simmer gently for 5 minutes. Remove the lid, stir and simmer for 2 minutes or until the fish is cooked but not breaking up.

Scatter over the parsley and serve with new potatoes.

tuna niçoise

serves 4

Free

ready in 30 minutes

Fill your plate with the sunshine of the French Riviera! This sparkling salad from Nice has so many fresh flavours to enjoy.

- 750g new potatoes, halved
- 4 eggs
- 300g trimmed green beans
- 4 tuna steaks
- low calorie cooking spray
- salt and freshly ground black pepper
- 2 Little Gem lettuces, leaves separated
- 200g cherry tomatoes, halved or quartered
- 125ml fat free vinaigrette

Cook the potatoes in a large saucepan of lightly salted boiling water for 12-15 minutes, adding the beans for the last 4 minutes. Drain well and transfer to a large salad bowl.

At the same time, cook the eggs to your liking in a saucepan of lightly salted boiling water (4 minutes for soft or up to 10 minutes for hard-boiled). Drain and transfer the eggs to a bowl of cold water – when they're cool enough to handle, peel and cut them into wedges.

Meanwhile, heat a non-stick griddle pan over a high heat until smoking hot. Spray the tuna steaks with low calorie cooking spray, season to taste and cook for 2-3 minutes on each side. Cut the tuna into bite-sized chunks and keep warm.

Add the lettuce leaves and tomatoes to the potatoes and beans, then scatter over the egg and tuna and season to taste.

Pour over the vinaigrette, toss to combine and serve warm.

For an even more authentic salad, add black olives – you can have eight for just 1½ Syns!

cauliflower gratin

serves 4

3½ Syns per serving

Ⓥ

ready in 30 minutes, plus standing

- 2 large cauliflowers, broken into florets
- low calorie cooking spray
- bunch of spring onions, thinly sliced
- 2 garlic cloves, chopped
- 500g fat free natural yogurt
- ½ tsp mustard powder
- 2 eggs, lightly beaten
- 80g reduced fat Cheddar cheese, coarsely grated
- salt and freshly ground black pepper
- 20g wholemeal bread, crumbed

In this fantastic vegetarian dish, tender cauliflower florets are smothered in a creamy sauce with a hint of mustard then baked with a crispy breadcrumb and cheese topping. Irresistible!

Preheat the oven to 220°C/Fan 200°C/Gas 7.

Cook the cauliflower in a saucepan of lightly salted boiling water for 3-4 minutes or until tender. Drain well and set aside.

Spray a large non-stick frying pan with low calorie cooking spray and place over a high heat. Add the spring onions, garlic and cauliflower florets and stir-fry for 2-3 minutes. Add 100ml of water to the pan and cook for 5 minutes or until the water has been absorbed. Transfer the mixture to a shallow ovenproof dish.

Mix the yogurt, mustard powder, eggs and two-thirds of the cheese in a bowl. Season to taste and pour over the cauliflower. Sprinkle over the breadcrumbs and remaining cheese and bake for 10 minutes or until lightly golden and bubbly. Remove from the oven and leave to stand for 5 minutes before serving with salad or your favourite vegetables.

puy lentils with sweet potato and goat's cheese

The colours in this splendid salad are a feast for the eyes and the combination of flavours is equally stunning.

serves 4

3 Syns per serving

V

ready in 40 minutes

---

4 beetroot, peeled and sliced

2 sweet potatoes,
peeled and sliced

low calorie cooking spray

salt and freshly ground
black pepper

300g dried Puy lentils

small bag of baby salad leaves

80g soft French goat's cheese,
roughly crumbled or chopped

for the dressing

small handful of finely
chopped fresh dill,
plus sprigs to garnish

1 garlic clove, crushed

3 tbsp white wine vinegar

1 level tsp Dijon mustard

a pinch of sweetener (optional)

200ml vegetable stock, cooled

Preheat the oven to 200°C/Fan 180°C/Gas 6.

Put the beetroot and sweet potatoes in a non-stick roasting tin, lightly spray with low calorie cooking spray, season and mix well. Roast for 25-30 minutes or until soft and cooked through, tossing the vegetables occasionally.

Meanwhile, put the Puy lentils in a large saucepan and fill with enough water to cover the lentils by 6-8cm. Place the pan over a high heat and bring to the boil, then reduce the heat, cover loosely with a lid and simmer for 15-20 minutes or until the lentils are tender.

While the lentils are cooking, mix all the dressing ingredients in a bowl and season to taste.

Drain the lentils and stir in two-thirds of the dressing. Check the seasoning, divide between plates and scatter over the beetroot, sweet potatoes, salad leaves and goat's cheese. Drizzle over the remaining dressing, garnish with the dill sprigs and serve warm or at room temperature.

potato dauphinoise

serves 4

Free

Ⓥ

ready in 1 hour 20 minutes

- low calorie cooking spray
- 1kg potatoes, peeled and thinly sliced
- 2 large onions, halved and thinly sliced
- 200g quark
- 250ml boiling vegetable stock
- 1 tbsp garlic salt
- freshly ground black pepper
- 2 tsp dried thyme

It's hard to beat roast potatoes but dauphinoise potatoes are definitely a contender! This simple and substantial side dish is usually made with lots of cream but our light version uses quark to make it completely Free!

Preheat the oven to 200°C/Fan 180°C/Gas 6.

Spray a medium-sized ovenproof dish with low calorie cooking spray.

Arrange half of the potatoes in the dish in an overlapping pattern, followed by a layer using up all the onions. Top with the remaining potatoes in the same overlapping pattern.

Put the quark, stock and garlic salt in a bowl and beat to make a smooth mixture. Season with black pepper and pour the mixture over the potatoes. Scatter over the thyme, spray lightly with low calorie cooking spray and bake for 50-60 minutes. (Check the top from time to time: if it's browning too quickly, cover with foil.)

Remove the dish from the oven and leave to rest for a few minutes before serving hot with your favourite meat or poultry and vegetables.

ratatouille

The key to a good ratatouille is to bake the aubergine and courgette separately, then stir everything together at the end. The fabulous colours and flavours make it amazing as a side dish with meat or fish.

serves 4

Free

ready in 40 minutes

---

1 large aubergine, cut into chunks

2 large courgettes, cut into chunks

2 tsp dried thyme

salt and freshly ground black pepper

low calorie cooking spray

1 red onion, roughly chopped

1 red pepper, halved, deseeded and cut into chunks

1 yellow pepper, halved, deseeded and cut into chunks

2 garlic cloves, crushed

400g can chopped tomatoes

1 bay leaf

2 tbsp red wine vinegar

small handful of roughly chopped fresh basil, to garnish

Preheat the oven to 190°C/Fan 170°C/Gas 5.

Put the aubergine and courgette into a roasting tin, sprinkle over the thyme and season to taste. Spray with low calorie cooking spray and roast until tender and starting to brown. This will take about 20-25 minutes.

Meanwhile, spray a large non-stick frying pan with low calorie cooking spray and place over a medium heat. Add the onion, peppers and garlic and cook until the onion and peppers have softened – about 15 minutes.

Add the tomatoes, bay leaf and wine vinegar to the onion and peppers. Season, stir well and simmer for another 15 minutes or until the tomatoes are nice and glossy.

Take the tomatoes off the heat, stir in the aubergines and courgettes and scatter over the basil. This is best served warm.

crêpes suzette

serves 4

5 Syns per serving

ready in 40 minutes

These sumptuous pancakes come with a deliciously sweet orange sauce and, unlike the traditional recipe, there's no need to set them alight before serving!

80g plain flour

1 tbsp sweetener

3 large eggs, beaten

250ml skimmed milk

¼ tsp vanilla extract

2 large oranges

low calorie cooking spray

fat free natural fromage frais, sweetened to taste, to serve

for the sauce

juice of 2 oranges

1 tsp sweetener

First make the sauce. Put the orange juice and sweetener in a small pan and stir over a gentle heat for 1-2 minutes or until the sweetener has dissolved.

For the crêpes, sift the flour and sweetener into a bowl. Mix in the eggs, milk and vanilla extract and grate in the zest of half an orange. Whisk until the mixture is smooth.

Peel and remove the pith from the oranges, then break them into segments and set aside.

Spray a small non-stick frying pan with low calorie cooking spray and place over a high heat. When hot, pour in one-eighth of the batter, tilting the pan to spread it around.

Cook for 1-2 minutes or until lightly browned underneath then flip over and cook the other side for 1-2 minutes. Remove the crêpe from the pan, fold into quarters and keep warm while you cook the remaining crêpes.

Divide the folded crêpes between plates, drizzle with the orange sauce and serve with the orange segments and a dollop of fromage frais.

raspberry clafoutis

serves 6

3 Syns per serving

ready in 45 minutes, plus cooling

low calorie cooking spray
600g raspberries
finely grated zest of ½ orange
4 tsp sweetener
3 eggs, separated
3 level tbsp plain flour
1 tsp vanilla extract
1 level tbsp ground almonds
3 tbsp skimmed milk
a pinch of salt
fat free natural fromage frais, sweetened to taste, to serve

This fantastic and very simple pudding comes from the Limousin region of France, where it is traditionally made with sour morello cherries. We've used raspberries for convenience.

Preheat the oven to 180°C/Fan 160°C/Gas 4.

Lightly spray a round, shallow 23cm baking dish with low calorie cooking spray. Add three-quarters of the raspberries and scatter over most of the orange zest and half the sweetener.

Beat the egg yolks and remaining sweetener together (with an electric hand mixer if you have one) until light and airy. Fold in the flour, vanilla extract, almonds and milk.

In a separate bowl, beat the egg whites with a pinch of salt until soft peaks form. Fold the whites gently into the batter until just blended.

Spoon the batter over the raspberries, scatter the remaining raspberries on top and bake on the middle shelf of the oven for 20-25 minutes or until the batter has puffed up and is lightly browned.

Remove from the oven and leave to cool a little. Scatter over the remaining orange zest and serve warm with fat free fromage frais.

This is amazing with a dusting of icing sugar (1 level teaspoon adds ½ Syn per serving).

cherry and vanilla brûlées

serves 4

5½ Syns per serving

ready in 20 minutes, plus cooling

Crème brûlée means burnt cream but there's nothing overdone about this sensational dessert. The contrast between the crisp, sugary topping and creaminess underneath is just heavenly!

- 1 vanilla pod, split lengthways
- 2 tbsp sweetener
- 400g cherries, pitted
- 400g fat free natural Greek yogurt
- 1 tsp vanilla extract
- 4 level tbsp caster sugar

Scrape the seeds from the vanilla pod into a small saucepan. Add 200ml of water and half the sweetener and bring to the boil over a high heat. Turn the heat to low and simmer gently for 5 minutes. Stir in the cherries and leave to cool.

Preheat the grill to high.

Mix together the yogurt, vanilla extract and remaining sweetener in a bowl.

Drain the cherries and divide them between four ramekins or small heatproof bowls. Top with the yogurt mixture, sprinkle the sugar evenly over each one and grill for 3-4 minutes or until the tops are golden and crisp.

Leave the brûlées to cool a little before serving.

Spain and Portugal

Give your tastebuds a holiday with a unique cuisine that offers so many delights, from mouth-watering 'tapas' starters to tempting tortillas, spicy chorizo sausages and perhaps the world's greatest rice dish, paella!

gazpacho

serves 4

Free

(without the fromage frais)

ready in 30 minutes, plus chilling

- 8 large ripe tomatoes
- 1 bottled roasted red pepper in brine, drained and roughly chopped
- 2 garlic cloves, crushed
- ¼ tsp sweetener (optional)
- 2-3 tbsp red wine vinegar
- a few drops of Tabasco
- salt and freshly ground black pepper
- ¼ cucumber
- fat free natural fromage frais, to serve
- 1 red pepper, halved, deseeded and finely diced

This chilled soup is a seriously refreshing summer treat. The riper the tomatoes you use, the better the flavour will be!

Score a cross in the base of each tomato and place in a bowl of boiling water for 10-15 seconds. Drain, plunge into cold water and peel off the skins. Cut the tomatoes in half then scoop out and discard the seeds. Roughly chop the flesh and put it in a food processor.

Add the red pepper, garlic, sweetener (if using), vinegar and Tabasco. Process until smooth, adding a little chilled water if you want a thinner soup. Season to taste and chill for 3-4 hours or overnight if you have time.

When you're ready to serve, halve the cucumber lengthways. Slice one half into thin batons and finely dice the rest. Pour the gazpacho into chilled glasses, add a dollop of fromage frais and garnish with the cucumber and pepper.

time for tapas!

Spain's famous small plates are perfect for sharing and make sensational starters! Turn the page for more tapas temptations…

romesco prawns

serves 4

Free

ready in 25 minutes, plus cooling

---

low calorie cooking spray

2 bottled roasted red peppers in brine, drained and cut into strips

1 dried red chilli

4 tomatoes, roughly chopped

4 garlic cloves, finely chopped

5 tbsp sherry vinegar

100g low fat natural cottage cheese

salt and freshly ground black pepper

24 peeled raw king or tiger prawns, with or without tails

small handful of roughly chopped fresh parsley, to garnish

Spray a large non-stick frying pan with low calorie cooking spray and place over a medium heat. Add the peppers, chilli, tomatoes and garlic and stir-fry for 5-6 minutes, then remove from the heat and cool for 10-15 minutes.

Preheat your grill to high.

Spoon the pepper mixture into a food processor and add the vinegar and cottage cheese. Season and whizz until smooth then transfer to a serving bowl.

Put the prawns on the grill rack and spray lightly with low calorie cooking spray. Grill them for 2-3 minutes on each side or until cooked through. Put the prawns into a serving dish, scatter over the parsley and serve hot with the sauce.

garlic mushrooms

serves 4

½ **Syn** per serving

V

ready in 25 minutes

---

low calorie cooking spray

400g button mushrooms, halved or quartered

½ red onion, finely chopped

6 garlic cloves, finely chopped

2 tbsp very dry sherry (fino is perfect)

150ml boiling vegetable stock

juice of 1 large lemon

1 tsp dried red chilli flakes

salt and freshly ground black pepper

small handful of roughly chopped fresh parsley, to garnish

Spray a large non-stick frying pan with low calorie cooking spray and place over a high heat. Add the mushrooms and onion and stir-fry for 5-6 minutes.

Add the garlic, sherry, stock, lemon juice and chilli, season to taste and cook for another 6-8 minutes.

Transfer the mushrooms to a serving dish and scatter over the parsley to serve.

chicken pinchitos

makes 12 skewers

Free

ready in 20 minutes, plus marinating

---

2 tsp ground cumin

1 tsp ground coriander

1 tsp sweet smoked paprika

2 tsp dried thyme

3 garlic cloves, crushed

juice of 1 lemon

salt

4 skinless chicken breasts, cut into chunks

2 red onions, cut into wedges

low calorie cooking spray

4 tomatoes, sliced

½ cucumber, sliced into ribbons with a peeler

Put the cumin, coriander, paprika, thyme, garlic and lemon juice in a bowl and add salt to taste. Add the chicken, stir to coat well then marinate in the fridge for 30 minutes or overnight if possible.

When you're ready to cook, preheat the grill to high.

Thread the chicken pieces and onion wedges on to 12 metal skewers (or use wooden skewers soaked in water for at least 20 minutes to stop them burning). Spray with low calorie cooking spray and grill for 4-5 minutes on each side or until cooked through.

Serve the pinchitos on a platter of sliced tomatoes and cucumber.

patatas bravas

serves 4

Free

ready in 30 minutes

1kg potatoes, peeled and cut into small chunks

low calorie cooking spray

salt and freshly ground black pepper

small handful of roughly chopped fresh parsley, to garnish

lemon wedges, to serve

for the tomato sauce

400g can chopped tomatoes

3 tbsp tomato purée

½ tsp sweetener

1 small red onion, finely chopped

2 garlic cloves, finely chopped

2 tsp smoked paprika

1 tsp cayenne pepper

1 bay leaf

Preheat your oven to 220°C/Fan 200°C/Gas 7 and line a roasting tin with non-stick baking parchment.

Boil the potatoes in a saucepan of lightly salted boiling water for 6-8 minutes, then drain and tip into the roasting tin. Spray with low calorie cooking spray, season and roast for 15-20 minutes or until golden.

Meanwhile, make the sauce. Put the tomatoes in a pan over a medium heat and add the tomato purée, sweetener, onion and garlic. Add 75ml of water and cook for 10-15 minutes. Stir in the spices and bay leaf and cook for 10 minutes or until thickened.

Tip the sauce into a shallow serving dish and pile the potatoes on top. Scatter over the parsley and serve with lemon wedges.

lamb cutlets with red peppers

Cutlets of lamb look so appealing and the peppers – fried with the distinctively Spanish flavours of paprika and sherry vinegar – are a match made in heaven!

serves 4

Free

SP

ready in 45 minutes

---

low calorie cooking spray

2 onions, halved and finely sliced

2 mild red chillies, deseeded and finely sliced

2 garlic cloves, crushed

3 red peppers, halved, deseeded and finely sliced

1 tsp hot smoked paprika

1 tbsp sherry vinegar

150ml boiling vegetable stock

salt and freshly ground black pepper

12 lamb cutlets, visible fat removed

Spray a large non-stick frying pan with low calorie cooking spray and place over a medium heat. Add the onions then cover and sweat gently for 10 minutes or until soft. Stir in the chillies, garlic, peppers, paprika, sherry vinegar and stock. Bring to the boil, cover and turn the heat to low. Cook gently for 30 minutes, stirring from time to time, until the peppers are soft. Season to taste and keep warm.

Meanwhile, put a non-stick griddle pan or large frying pan over a high heat. Spray the lamb cutlets with low calorie cooking spray and fry for 2-3 minutes on each side until they are brown on the outside but pink and juicy inside (you may need to cook them in batches). Season the lamb to taste.

Divide the peppers between warmed plates, top with the lamb cutlets and serve with extra vegetables.

piri piri lamb with rice salad

serves 4

Free

ready in 20 minutes

8 lean lamb leg steaks (or 12 for a meat feast!), visible fat removed

1 tbsp piri piri seasoning

low calorie cooking spray

lime wedges, to serve

for the rice salad

350g dried long-grain rice

½ cucumber, roughly chopped

1 red chilli, deseeded and finely chopped

1 red onion, finely chopped

1 bottled roasted red pepper in brine, drained and roughly chopped

small handful of roughly chopped fresh mint

salt and freshly ground black pepper

The Portuguese love their chillies and the most popular choice is piri piri, a scorching-hot African variety! Our recipe uses just a little piri piri seasoning, so everyone can enjoy that warmth and flavour.

Cook the rice according to the packet instructions. Drain, rinse under cold water and transfer to a salad bowl. Mix in the remaining salad ingredients and season to taste.

Meanwhile, season the lamb with the piri piri seasoning and spray with low calorie cooking spray. Place a large non-stick griddle pan or frying pan over a high heat. When it's smoking-hot, cook the steaks for 3-4 minutes on each side if thin or 4-5 minutes each side if thick, or until done to your liking.

Divide the rice salad between plates and serve with the steaks and lime wedges.

fabada asturiana

-asturian pork stew-

This satisfying hotpot from the north of Spain is packed with filling meat and beans.

serves 4

Free

ready in 1 hour

- low calorie cooking spray
- 600g lean pork fillet, visible fat removed, cut into chunks
- 1 onion, sliced
- 1 red chilli, deseeded and finely chopped
- 2 tsp sweet smoked paprika
- a large pinch of saffron strands (or use ½ tsp turmeric)
- 4 garlic cloves, crushed
- 100ml boiling vegetable stock
- 400g can chopped tomatoes
- 400g can butter beans or haricot beans, drained and rinsed
- 400g can red kidney beans, drained and rinsed
- small handful of finely chopped fresh parsley, to garnish
- salt and freshly ground black pepper

Spray a large non-stick saucepan (that has a lid) with low calorie cooking spray and place over a medium heat. Add the pork and fry for 4-5 minutes so it's nicely browned but not cooked through, then transfer to a warm plate with a slotted spoon.

Add the onion and chilli to the same pan and fry for 2-3 minutes or until softened. Add the paprika, saffron, garlic, stock, tomatoes and beans, then return the cooked pork to the pan and stir well.

Bring the mixture to a gentle simmer over a low heat, cover with a lid and cook for 45 minutes or until the sauce has thickened. Add a few tablespoons of water now and again if the sauce is looking dry.

Ladle the stew into warmed shallow bowls, sprinkle over the parsley and season with salt and freshly ground black pepper. This is fantastic served hot with rice and salad.

lentejas

-lentil and chorizo stew-

serves 4

3 Syns per serving

❄

ready in 1 hour

250g dried green lentils, washed and drained

1 leek, trimmed and thinly sliced

2 carrots, peeled and finely diced

2 garlic cloves, finely chopped

1 tbsp sweet smoked paprika

2 onions, finely chopped

salt and freshly ground black pepper

low calorie cooking spray

120g chorizo, roughly chopped or sliced

2 plum tomatoes, deseeded and finely chopped

small handful of roughly chopped fresh parsley, to garnish

Spicy chorizo sausage is one of the unmistakable flavours of Spain and it adds so much flavour to this fabulously filling stew.

Place the lentils in a large saucepan with 800ml of water. Add the leek, carrots, garlic, sweet paprika and half of the onions. Season to taste and bring to a simmer over a very low heat. Cover and cook for 45-50 minutes or until the lentils are tender. (If you prefer a stew that's more like a soup, add a little more boiling water to the pan if the level gets too low.)

About 15 minutes before the lentils are done, spray a non-stick frying pan with low calorie cooking spray and place over a medium heat. Sauté the chorizo and remaining onions until lightly browned, then stir the chorizo mixture and tomatoes into the lentils, scatter over the parsley and serve hot.

Most large supermarkets sell dry-cured chorizo rings, which are perfect for this recipe.

cocido madrileño

-chicken and chickpea stew-

serves 4

Free

❄ *SP*

ready in 2 hours

---

6 chicken drumsticks

6 skinless chicken thighs

1 garlic bulb

8 back bacon rashers, visible fat removed, roughly chopped

1 tbsp sweet smoked paprika

1 large onion, roughly chopped

1.5 litres boiling chicken stock

2 large carrots, peeled and cut into chunks

4 celery sticks, thickly sliced

2 x 400g cans chickpeas, drained and rinsed

¼ green cabbage, finely shredded

small handful of finely chopped fresh parsley, to garnish

Known as a cocido in Spain and a cozido in Portugal, these sumptuous stews are ideal for winter feasts. This version from Madrid includes chickpeas plus loads of tempting chicken pieces and bacon – and it's completely Free!

Skin the chicken drumsticks by pulling the skin from the thicker end over the bony end (use a piece of kitchen paper to get a good grip).

Put all of the chicken, garlic, bacon, paprika, onion, stock, carrots, celery and half the chickpeas in a heavy-based saucepan and bring to the boil over a high heat. Cover tightly, reduce the heat to low and cook for 1½ hours or until the chicken is almost falling off the bone.

Season to taste and stir in the remaining chickpeas and the cabbage. Bring to a boil and cook for 6-8 minutes. Remove from the heat, discard the garlic bulb and scatter over the parsley. Ladle into warmed shallow bowls to serve.

For an even more authentic flavour, use 100g roughly chopped Serrano ham instead of bacon, adding 1½ Syns per serving.

mixed paella

serves 4

Free

ready in 40 minutes

- low calorie cooking spray
- 1 onion, finely chopped
- 2 garlic cloves, finely chopped
- 4 skinless and boneless chicken breasts, cut into bite-sized pieces
- large pinch of saffron threads (optional)
- ¼ tsp turmeric
- 900ml boiling chicken stock
- 1 tbsp smoked paprika
- 250g dried paella rice
- 200g live mussels
- 200g fresh squid rings (or use frozen and thawed)
- 12 cooked and peeled king prawns, with or without tails
- 2 bottled roasted red peppers in brine, drained and roughly chopped
- 100g frozen peas
- 2 large carrots, peeled and finely diced
- salt and freshly ground black pepper
- small handful of finely chopped fresh parsley, to garnish
- lemon wedges, to serve

Spain's most famous dish is traditionally made in three ways. The original recipe – Valencian paella – uses chicken, rabbit and vegetables (and sometimes snails!), while seafood paella uses shellfish in their shells. Mixed paella offers the best of both worlds!

Spray a paella pan or large non-stick frying pan with low calorie cooking spray and place over a medium-low heat. Add the onion, garlic and chicken and stir-fry for 5 minutes or until softened.

Stir the saffron threads (if using) and turmeric into the stock, then add the stock to the pan and stir in the smoked paprika. Bring to a simmer then add the paella rice. Stir once, then cover and leave to simmer gently for 15-20 minutes.

Scrub the mussels, pulling off any beards, and discard any that are damaged or are open but don't close when tapped against the sink.

Add the mussels, squid, prawns, peppers, peas and carrots to the paella. Cook for a further 10 minutes, stirring occasionally, until the rice is soft but not mushy, the vegetables are tender and the mussels have opened (discard any that remain closed). Season to taste, scatter over the parsley and serve in shallow bowls with lemon wedges to squeeze over.

If you want to save time you can use 2 x 225g seafood selection packs (these usually contain squid, mussels and prawns) instead of buying them separately. Add to the paella and heat through for the last 5-6 minutes.

crusted cod with judías verdes

A crispy coating of breadcrumbs infused with lemon and garlic takes cod to another level and the judías verdes – Spanish-style green beans – are a great accompaniment.

serves 4

1½ Syns per serving

ready in 35 minutes

---

4 thick cod fillets, skinned

60g wholemeal bread, crumbed

finely grated zest of 1 unwaxed lemon

small handful of finely chopped fresh parsley

1 tbsp chopped fresh chives

1 garlic clove, finely chopped

for the judías verdes

1 tbsp white wine vinegar

300g green beans, trimmed

low calorie cooking spray

1 red onion, finely chopped

2 garlic cloves, finely chopped

salt and freshly ground black pepper

2 tomatoes, deseeded and roughly chopped

First make the judías verdes. Bring a saucepan of lightly salted water to the boil over a high heat. Add the vinegar and green beans, bring back to the boil and cook for 3-4 minutes. Drain, refresh the beans in cold water and drain again. Pat the beans dry with kitchen paper.

Spray a large non-stick frying pan with low calorie cooking spray and place over a medium heat. Add the red onion and green beans and fry for 3-4 minutes, then add the garlic and fry for 1 more minute. Season to taste, cover the pan and reduce the heat to very low. Cook for 5-6 minutes then remove from the heat and stir in the tomatoes. Set aside and keep warm.

Meanwhile, preheat the oven to 220°C/Fan 200°C/Gas 7.

Season the cod on both sides and arrange on a baking tray lined with non-stick baking parchment.

Put the breadcrumbs, lemon zest, parsley, chives and garlic into a bowl and season to taste. Mix together well then press the crumbs on to the fillets in a thick, even layer. Spray with low calorie cooking spray and bake for 10-12 minutes or until the crust is crisp and lightly golden and the fish is cooked through. Lift on to warm plates and serve with the judías verdes and your favourite potatoes.

sardinas murcianas
-baked sardines and potatoes-

serves 4
Free
ready in 1 hour

Sardines are affordable, healthy and hugely popular in Spain and Portugal. Enjoy them at their best in this easy-to-make baked dish from the Spanish coastal region of Murcia.

- low calorie cooking spray
- 2 large onions, sliced
- 4 garlic cloves, finely chopped
- 1 red pepper, deseeded and finely chopped
- 400g can chopped tomatoes
- 1 tsp hot smoked paprika
- a large pinch of saffron threads (optional)
- 1 tsp ground cumin
- 1 cinnamon stick
- 1 bay leaf
- small handful of finely chopped fresh parsley, plus extra to garnish
- salt and freshly ground black pepper
- 750g floury potatoes, such as King Edward, peeled and thinly sliced
- 12 sardines, cleaned, heads and tails removed and butterflied (ask your fishmonger to do this for you)

Preheat your oven to 200°C/Fan 180°C/Gas 6.

Spray a large non-stick frying pan with low calorie cooking spray and place over a medium-low heat. Stir-fry the onions, garlic and pepper for 10-15 minutes then add the tomatoes, spices, bay leaf and parsley. Season and cook for 10 minutes, stirring occasionally.

Meanwhile, cook the potatoes in lightly salted boiling water for 5 minutes and drain well.

Lightly season the cavity of each sardine. Spread half of the tomato sauce on the base of a shallow, ovenproof dish. Add a layer using half the potato slices then another layer using all the sardines. Spread the remaining sauce over the fish and finish with a layer of potatoes. Spray with low calorie cooking spray and bake for 15-20 minutes or until the fish flakes easily.

Add a good grind of black pepper, scatter over the extra parsley and serve hot with salad.

trout with serrano ham and red cabbage

One of Spain's favourite delicacies, Serrano ham is dry-cured and thinly sliced, and its deep flavour goes brilliantly with trout.

serves 4

½ **Syn** per serving

ready in 45 minutes

---

low calorie cooking spray

12 back bacon rashers, visible fat removed, roughly chopped

1 onion, finely chopped

3 garlic cloves, crushed

½ red cabbage, finely shredded

1 tsp sweet smoked paprika

salt and freshly ground black pepper

4 slices of Serrano ham

4 large trout fillets

lemon wedges, to serve

Spray a large, non-stick frying pan with low calorie cooking spray and place over a high heat. Add the bacon and stir-fry for 2-3 minutes.

Stir in the onion, garlic and red cabbage and stir-fry for 5-6 minutes. Add the paprika and stir to mix well. Pour over just enough water to cover the cabbage and cook over a medium heat for 20-25 minutes or until most of the liquid has evaporated. Season to taste and keep warm.

Meanwhile, preheat the grill to medium-high.

Spread out the ham on the grill rack and cook for 3-4 minutes or until crisp. Set aside and keep warm.

Put the trout fillets on the grill rack, season to taste and spray with low calorie cooking spray. Grill for 8-10 minutes or until cooked through.

Divide the cabbage mixture between warmed plates, add the grilled trout and top with the crispy ham. Serve hot with salad and lemon wedges to squeeze over.

zarzuela

~catalan fish stew~

serves 4

Free

ready in 40 minutes

---

low calorie cooking spray

12 peeled raw king or tiger prawns, with or without tails

1 onion, finely chopped

4 garlic cloves, crushed

4 tomatoes, roughly chopped

1 bay leaf

a large pinch of saffron (optional)

1 tsp sweet smoked paprika

1 dried red chilli

250ml boiling fish stock

400g firm white fish fillets, cut into bite-sized pieces

225g pack of seafood selection (eg squid, mussels, prawns)

560g can peeled new potatoes in water, drained and halved

small handful of finely chopped fresh parsley, to garnish

salt and freshly ground black pepper

This tasty stew brings together a variety of fish and shellfish in a delicious broth – feel free to swap in other seafood if you like. We've added potatoes to make it really filling but rice on the side would work well too!

Spray a large non-stick frying pan with low calorie cooking spray and place over a high heat. Add the prawns and cook for 3-4 minutes or until they start to turn pink, then remove with a slotted spoon and set aside on a plate.

Add the onion and half the garlic to the pan and cook gently for 10 minutes or until the onion has softened.

Add the tomatoes, bay leaf, saffron (if using), paprika, chilli and stock and bring to the boil. Turn the heat to low, add the fish and cook for 5 minutes. Add the seafood pack and potatoes and cook for another 3-4 minutes to heat through.

Stir in the remaining garlic and return the prawns and any juices to the pan. Stir to mix and ladle into shallow bowls. Scatter over the parsley, season to taste and eat hot.

tortilla española

~spanish omelette~

serves 4

Free

Ⓥ

ready in 30 minutes

This simple Spanish classic is a cousin of the French omelette but with the important addition of potatoes to make it seriously satisfying, and plenty of tasty veg to make it totally delicious!

- low calorie cooking spray
- 1 red pepper, halved, deseeded and thinly sliced
- 1 yellow pepper, halved, deseeded and thinly sliced
- 1 orange pepper, halved, deseeded and thinly sliced
- 1 large onion, finely sliced
- 560g can peeled new potatoes in water, drained and sliced
- 6 large eggs, beaten
- salt and freshly ground black pepper
- 1 tsp dried thyme
- small handful of chopped fresh chives
- pinch of paprika, to garnish

Place a non-stick frying pan over a medium-high heat and spray with low calorie cooking spray. Add the peppers and onion and stir-fry for 6-7 minutes or until they're starting to soften. Add the potatoes and turn the heat to low.

Preheat the grill to high.

Pour the eggs over the vegetables in the frying pan. Season to taste, scatter over the thyme and chives and cook for 5 minutes.

Put the pan under the grill for 1-2 minutes until the top of the omelette is set and golden, then sprinkle with the paprika and cut into wedges.

This is great with a crisp green salad.

suspiros
~meringue kisses~

makes 20 suspiros

1 Syn each

Ⓥ

ready in 2 hours 45 minutes, plus chilling and cooling

200g quark

3 large egg whites

120g caster sugar

1 level tsp cream of tartar

1 tsp sweetener

a few drops of vanilla extract

mixed berries, to serve

Suspiros means sighs in Spanish and that's the effect these tasty nibbles will have on anyone who tries them!

Line a sieve with muslin (or a clean tea towel) and set over a bowl. Put the quark into the muslin, tie up to form a bundle and squeeze to drain off any excess liquid. Chill, then squeeze again once the meringues have been in the oven for 1 hour and once more when they are done.

Preheat the oven to the lowest possible heat and line two baking sheets with non-stick baking parchment.

Put the egg whites in a large glass mixing bowl. Beat them on a medium speed with an electric hand whisk until the mixture forms stiff peaks when the blades are lifted out. Turn the speed to high and start to add the sugar a spoonful at a time, beating for 3-4 seconds between each spoonful. When the mixture is thick, glossy and smooth, whisk in the cream of tartar until well blended.

Using a piping bag with a fluted nozzle, pipe 40 rounds on to the prepared baking sheets, leaving space between each one. Bake for 2 hours or until the meringues are crisp. Leave to cool on the trays or a cooling rack.

Make the filling by mixing the quark with the sweetener and vanilla. When the meringues are cool, sandwich two together with a dollop of the filling and repeat to use up all the meringues. Serve with mixed berries and dust with icing sugar, if you like (1 level teaspoon is 1 Syn).

spanish orange cake

The whole family will enjoy this special cake! Oranges are everywhere in Spain and in many towns you'll see orange trees lining the streets, especially in southern cities like Seville.

serves 10

4 Syns per serving

Ⓥ

ready in 1 hour, plus cooling

low calorie cooking spray

4 eggs, separated

50g golden caster sugar

5 tbsp sweetener

2 tbsp finely grated orange zest and the juice of 2 oranges, plus orange segments to decorate

150g self-raising flour

1 level tsp baking powder

for the syrup

pared zest of 1 orange and 120ml of freshly squeezed orange juice

1 level tsp arrowroot

1 tbsp sweetener

1 level tsp caster sugar

Preheat the oven to 180°C/Fan 160°C/Gas 4. Line a 20cm loose-bottomed sandwich tin with non-stick baking parchment and spray with a little low calorie cooking spray.

Put the egg yolks, sugar, sweetener and grated orange zest and juice in a bowl and whisk until thick and pale.

Whisk the egg whites in a separate bowl until soft peaks form then fold into the egg yolk mixture. Sieve the flour and baking powder into another bowl then tip into the eggs and stir in very gently. Spoon this mixture into the prepared cake tin and bake for 25-30 minutes or until the cake has risen and is firm to the touch. Set aside to cool.

Meanwhile, put the syrup ingredients in a small saucepan over a high heat and bring to the boil, whisking constantly. When it starts to thicken, remove from the heat and cool slightly.

Decorate the cake with orange segments, drizzle over the sauce and cut into slices to serve.

flan

-caramel custard-

serves 6

4 Syns per serving

Ⓥ

ready in 1 hour 25 minutes, plus cooling and chilling

---

4 level tbsp caster sugar

600ml skimmed milk

4 eggs plus one extra yolk, beaten

1 tsp vanilla essence

3 tbsp sweetener or to taste

a little freshly grated nutmeg

mixed berries, to serve

The Spanish sister of crème caramel is irresistibly creamy – and it's a favourite across South and Central America too.

Preheat the oven to 160°C/Fan 140°C/Gas 3.

Put the sugar into a non-stick saucepan over a medium heat and cook until the sugar has turned into a golden liquid, stirring occasionally and taking care not to let it burn. This will take 10-15 minutes. When it's ready, add a few tablespoons of hot water, mix well and pour the mixture into an ovenproof dish.

Pour the milk into the saucepan you used for the caramel and heat until warm, whisking occasionally.

Whisk the eggs in a large bowl, then whisk in the hot milk, vanilla essence and sweetener. Sieve the mixture into a clean jug, pour into the ovenproof dish and sprinkle with nutmeg.

Place the dish in a deep baking tin and pour in boiling water to come no higher than three-quarters of the way up the side of the dish. Bake for about 1 hour or until set then remove from the oven. Leave to cool and chill overnight.

Run a palette knife around the edges of the flan, put a serving plate on top and flip it over to turn out. Pour over any caramel left in the dish and serve with mixed berries.

North Africa

The fragrant food of Morocco, Tunisia, Egypt, Libya and Algeria is infused with the heat of the desert. Chilli and smoky spices add unbelievable flavours to our lamb, chicken and seafood dishes – and almost all of them are completely Free!

moroccan-spiced squid

serves 4

Free

ready in 20 minutes, plus marinating

700g prepared large squid tubes, tentacles removed (save the tentacles and fry them with lemon and garlic)

low calorie cooking spray

for the marinade

large handful of fresh coriander, plus extra, roughly chopped, to garnish

large handful of fresh parsley

1 tsp paprika

1 tsp ground coriander

1 tsp ground cumin

1 tsp cayenne pepper

4 garlic cloves, crushed

4 tbsp fat free natural yogurt

juice of 1 lime, plus lime halves to serve

salt and freshly ground black pepper

Fresh squid is so tender when it's cooked briefly and this mouth-watering marinade perfectly complements its subtle flavour.

First make the marinade. Put the herbs in a food processor with the spices, garlic, yogurt and lime juice. Season to taste, blend to make a smooth paste and transfer to a large bowl.

Cut the squid tubes open on one side and press them flat. Using a sharp knife, score a diamond pattern into each one (this helps to tenderise the squid). Cut the squid into large pieces and add to the marinade, stirring to coat well. Cover and marinate in the fridge for 4 hours or overnight if possible.

When you're ready to eat, spray a non-stick griddle pan or frying pan with low calorie cooking spray and place over a high heat. Cook the squid for 2-3 minutes, turning halfway, then divide between plates, scatter over the extra coriander and serve hot with lime halves and a tomato salad.

If you can't find squid tubes at your supermarket or fishmonger, you can use frozen squid rings, thawed, instead.

harira

serves 4

Free

❄ Ⓥ

ready in 2 hours

This filling and fragrant Moroccan soup is much-loved across North Africa. It's especially popular during the Islamic festival of Ramadan, when it is eaten at sunset as the daily fast comes to an end.

- 1 onion, chopped
- 1 celery stick, trimmed and chopped
- 1.5 litres boiling vegetable stock
- 1 tsp turmeric
- 1 tsp paprika
- 1 tsp ground cinnamon
- 4 tomatoes, chopped
- 100g dried split red lentils
- 100g dried vermicelli pasta
- 400g can chickpeas, drained
- salt and freshly ground black pepper
- small handful of finely chopped fresh parsley
- small handful of finely chopped fresh coriander
- lemon wedges, to serve

Put the onion and celery in a large saucepan with 300ml of the stock. Cover the pan and bring to the boil over a high heat. Cook for 5-10 minutes, then reduce the heat to low, uncover and simmer for 20 minutes or until the vegetables are tender, golden and syrupy.

Stir in the spices and cook for 2 minutes then add the tomatoes and lentils. Cook for 5 minutes, stirring occasionally, then add the remaining stock and simmer for 1 hour (or up to 2 hours if you have time).

Add the pasta and chickpeas and simmer for 15 minutes. Just before serving, season to taste and stir in the chopped herbs.

Enjoy this soup hot with lemon wedges and a dollop of harissa paste if you want to add some heat (see page 96).

egg and roast pepper salad

serves 4

½ **Syn** per serving

V

ready in 20 minutes, plus cooling

- 1 red onion, thinly sliced
- juice of 1 lemon
- 2 red peppers, halved and deseeded
- 2 yellow peppers, halved and deseeded
- 4 eggs
- 6 tomatoes, cut into wedges
- 1 tbsp capers, drained and rinsed
- 8 olives, thinly sliced
- salt and freshly ground black pepper
- small handful of roughly chopped fresh parsley, to garnish

Juicy peppers are a big part of North African cuisine and this beautiful salad really makes the most of them.

Preheat the grill to high.

Put the onion and lemon juice into a large bowl and stir well (the lemon juice will soften the onion).

Arrange the peppers on the grill pan, skin side up, and grill for 10 minutes or until the skin begins to char. Transfer the peppers to a bowl, cover with cling film and set aside for 10-15 minutes (this will make them easier to peel).

Meanwhile, cook the eggs to your liking in a saucepan of lightly salted boiling water (4 minutes for soft up to 10 minutes for hard-boiled). Drain the eggs and plunge them into cold water to cool (this will make them easy to peel). When the eggs are cool enough to handle, peel and roughly chop them. Add to the onion, along with the tomatoes, capers and olives.

Peel the peppers, slice them thickly and stir them into the salad.

Divide the salad between plates, season to taste and scatter over the parsley to serve.

harissa paste

We've created a completely Free version of North Africa's famous fiery paste – plus three spicy recipes to use it in, which you'll find below and over the page.

makes about 250g **Free** V SP ready in 10 minutes

- 3 tsp caraway seeds
- 3 tsp cumin seeds
- 4 garlic cloves, peeled
- 2 red chillies, halved and deseeded (use less for a milder flavour)
- pinch of sea salt
- 1 bottled roasted red pepper in brine, drained
- 4 tsp passata
- 4 tsp red wine vinegar
- juice of 2 lemons
- 2 tsp smoked paprika

Grind the spice seeds and garlic using a pestle and mortar (or rolling pin) and put the mixture into a food processor along with the chillies, sea salt, red pepper, passata and vinegar. Blend until smooth and transfer to a mixing bowl.

Add the lemon juice and paprika and stir well. Season with more salt to balance the vinegar, if necessary, and spoon into a clean screwtop jar. It will keep in the fridge for up to a week.

harissa king prawns

serves 4 **Free** ❄ ready in 20 minutes

- 40 peeled raw tiger or king prawns, with or without tails
- 6 tbsp harissa paste (see recipe, above)
- 8 bay leaves

Tip the prawns into a bowl, add the harissa paste and toss to coat well. (They'll taste even better if you leave them to marinate for 30 minutes.)

Thread the prawns and a bay leaf on to eight metal skewers (or wooden skewers soaked in water for 20 minutes to stop them burning).

Place a griddle pan over a high heat – when smoking hot, add the skewers and cook for 5 minutes, turning and basting occasionally.

Serve sizzling hot with couscous and salad.

Couscous is really tasty tossed with chopped tomatoes, red onion, cucumber and fresh coriander.

harissa lamb

serves 4 **Free**  ready in 15 minutes

8 tbsp harissa paste (see previous page)

1 tbsp tomato purée

8 lean lamb leg steaks, visible fat removed

lemon wedges, to serve

Preheat your grill to medium.

Mix together the harissa paste and tomato purée in a bowl.

Arrange the lamb on the grill pan and use half of the harissa to coat the top of the lamb steaks. Grill for 5 minutes then turn, top with the remaining harissa and grill for another 5 minutes.

Serve with lemon wedges and your favourite vegetables.

harissa chicken

serves 4 **Free**  ready in 45 minutes

4 chicken drumsticks

4 skinless chicken thighs

8 tbsp harissa paste (see previous page)

small bag of rocket leaves, to serve

Preheat the oven to 200°C/Fan 180°C/Gas 6.

Skin each drumstick by pulling the skin over the bony end (using a piece of kitchen paper will help you get a good grip). With a sharp knife, make a few slashes in each chicken drumstick and put them in a non-stick roasting tin along with the chicken thighs.

Rub the harissa over the chicken pieces, making sure to get plenty into the cuts. (If you have time, leave the chicken to marinate for 30 minutes to deepen the flavour.) Roast for 35-40 minutes or until cooked through.

Serve the chicken hot on a bed of rocket leaves with your favourite vegetables.

lamb tagine

Tagines are stews that take their name from the traditional Moroccan earthenware pots they're cooked in, though they'll taste just as great made in a casserole pan. Almost anything can go into a tagine – for this one we've used lamb, carrots and courgettes.

serves 4

Free

ready in 1 hour 15 minutes

---

low calorie cooking spray

1 onion, finely chopped

1 tbsp ground cumin

2 tsp ground cinnamon

1 tsp turmeric

2 tsp coriander

1 tsp dried red chilli flakes

500g lean lamb leg steaks, visible fat removed, cut into bite-sized pieces

400g can chopped tomatoes

2 tbsp tomato purée

2 tsp sweetener

4 carrots, peeled and cut into chunks

2 courgettes, halved lengthways and sliced

salt and freshly ground black pepper

small handful of finely chopped fresh coriander, to garnish

Spray a non-stick casserole pan with low calorie cooking spray and place over a high heat. Add the onion, spices and lamb and stir-fry for 5-6 minutes.

Add the tomatoes, tomato purée and sweetener and bring to the boil. Reduce the heat to low then cover and simmer for 35-40 minutes or until the meat is tender.

Stir in the carrots and courgettes and cook for a further 15 minutes or until the vegetables are tender. Season to taste, scatter over the coriander and serve hot.

spiced chicken and courgette couscous

serves 4

Free

ready in 30 minutes

It's the warming spices that make this satisfying supper so memorable. Close your eyes and you can almost see the Sahara!

- 4 garlic cloves, crushed
- 2 tsp dried red chilli flakes
- 1 tsp ground cinnamon
- 1 tbsp ras el hanout spice mix
- salt and freshly ground black pepper
- juice of 1 lemon
- 4 skinless and boneless chicken breasts
- 2 courgettes, sliced
- low calorie cooking spray
- 500g dried couscous
- 6 tomatoes, roughly chopped
- small handful of roughly chopped fresh mint

Preheat the oven to 200°C/Fan 180°C/Gas 6.

Put the garlic, chilli, cinnamon and ras el hanout in a shallow bowl and season to taste. Stir in the lemon juice and add the chicken breasts, rolling them around to coat well.

Arrange the chicken breasts and courgette pieces in a roasting tin, spray with low calorie cooking spray and roast for 25 minutes or until the chicken is cooked through and the courgettes are tender.

Meanwhile, put the couscous into a bowl and pour over enough boiling water to just cover. Leave for about 10 minutes or until the water is absorbed then fluff up the grains with a fork. Stir in the tomatoes, roasted courgettes and mint and divide between plates.

Slice the chicken breasts and arrange the pieces alongside the couscous. This is sensational served with a spoonful of harissa paste (see page 96).

Ras el hanout is a classic Moroccan blend of aromatic spices and is available in most large supermarkets. If you can't find any, an Indian curry powder will be just as aromatic and tasty.

chicken and preserved lemon tagine

serves 4

Free

❄

ready in 1 hour

Pickling lemons softens their flavour and texture, making them delicious in savoury meals such as tagines – the region's classic stews.

- low calorie cooking spray
- 8 skinless and boneless chicken thighs, visible fat removed, cut into large chunks
- 1 onion, finely chopped
- 3 carrots, peeled and cut into chunks
- 2 garlic cloves, crushed
- 1 tsp ground cumin
- ½ tsp turmeric
- ½ tsp paprika
- ½ tsp ground cinnamon
- 600ml boiling chicken stock
- 400g can chickpeas, drained and rinsed
- 4 preserved lemons, sliced
- small handful of roughly chopped fresh coriander

Preheat the oven to 180°C/Fan 160°C/Gas 4.

Place a large non-stick casserole pan over a medium-high heat and spray with low calorie cooking spray. Add the chicken, onion and carrots and cook for 10 minutes or until the chicken is lightly browned and the onion has softened.

Add the garlic and spices and cook for 1 minute, stirring.

Pour in the stock and add the chickpeas and the lemon slices. Bring to the boil and cover with a lid, then transfer to the oven and cook for 40 minutes.

Divide the tagine between shallow bowls, scatter over the coriander and serve with plenty of couscous and your favourite vegetables.

Preserved lemons are available in some larger supermarkets, stocked in the world food section, but if you can't find any, use six strips of lemon rind instead.

moroccan fish balls in tomato sauce

serves 4

Free

SP

ready in 1 hour, plus standing

These sensational fish balls are infused with warming spices and served in a mouth-watering sauce. Any white fish will work well in this recipe.

800g skinless white fish fillets

1 onion, cut into chunks

2 garlic cloves

small handful of fresh coriander

2 tsp ground cumin

1 egg, beaten

low calorie cooking spray

small handful of shredded fresh mint, to garnish

lemon wedges, to serve

for the tomato sauce

1 tsp ground cumin

1 tsp sweet paprika

1 tsp dried red chilli flakes

1 tsp ground coriander

1 tsp ground ginger

1 onion, finely chopped

150ml boiling vegetable stock

400g can chopped tomatoes

2 garlic cloves, crushed

salt and freshly ground black pepper

Preheat the oven to 200°C/Fan 180°C/Gas 6 and line a baking tray with non-stick baking parchment.

Put the fish, onion, garlic, coriander, cumin and egg in a food processor and blend until fairly smooth. Transfer to a bowl and, using your hands, shape the mixture into 24 balls. (If the mixture is too wet to form balls, chill it for at least 30 minutes to firm it up first.) Arrange the fish balls on the baking tray, spray with low calorie cooking spray and bake for 20 minutes.

Meanwhile, make the tomato sauce. Spray a wide non-stick saucepan with low calorie cooking spray and place over a medium heat. Add the spices and onion and cook for 10 minutes or until the onion has softened. Add the stock and simmer for 2-3 minutes then add the tomatoes and garlic. Season with salt and freshly ground black pepper and simmer for 15 minutes or until quite thick.

Remove the fish balls from the oven and stir them into the tomato sauce. Cover the pan, turn the heat to very low and simmer for 15-20 minutes.

Turn off the heat and leave the balls to stand, uncovered, for at least 10 minutes. Scatter with the mint and serve hot or warm with lemon wedges and salad.

tuna with tunisian aubergine salad

This refreshing dish comes from Tunisia, at the western end of the Mediterranean, and the smoky flavour you get by griddling the tuna and the aubergine is out of this world!

serves 4

Free

SP

ready in 25 minutes

1 large aubergine, thinly sliced

low calorie cooking spray

salt and freshly ground black pepper

4 tuna steaks

6 plum tomatoes, roughly chopped

1 red onion, halved and finely sliced

small handful of finely chopped fresh mint

small handful of finely chopped fresh parsley, to garnish

for the dressing

2 garlic cloves, finely chopped

½ tsp dried red chilli flakes

¼ tsp ground cumin

¼ tsp dried oregano

finely grated zest and juice of 1 unwaxed lemon, plus wedges to serve

200ml vegetable stock, cooled

Lightly spray the aubergine slices with low calorie cooking spray and season to taste with salt and freshly ground black pepper.

Place a non-stick griddle pan over a high heat. When it's smoking-hot, add the aubergine slices and cook for 2-3 minutes on each side until tender and nicely charred. Transfer the slices to a mixing bowl and cover with cling film.

Cook the tuna steaks to your liking on the hot griddle pan (2-3 minutes each side for rare or 3-4 minutes each side for well done).

Meanwhile, mix all the dressing ingredients in a small bowl and season to taste.

Add the tomatoes and red onion to the aubergine, pour over the dressing and toss to mix well.

Divide the tuna steaks and salad vegetables between plates, scatter over the fresh herbs and serve with extra vegetables, if you like.

chermoula fish skewers

serves 4

Free

ready in 40 minutes, plus marinating

4 thick skinless white fish fillets, cut into bite-sized chunks

1 green pepper, halved, deseeded and cut into bite-sized pieces

1 red pepper, halved, deseeded and cut into bite-sized pieces

1 yellow pepper, halved, deseeded and cut into bite-sized pieces

small handful of roughly chopped fresh mint, to garnish

for the chermoula

1 tsp sweet paprika

large handful of finely chopped fresh coriander, plus extra to garnish

1 tsp ground coriander

small handful of finely chopped fresh parsley

2 tsp ground cumin

6 garlic cloves, crushed

juice of 2 limes, plus wedges to serve

1 small red onion, finely chopped

1 tsp cayenne pepper

salt and freshly ground black pepper

Chermoula is a sensational fish marinade used across North Africa. As with most marinades, the longer you can wait before cooking, the better your dinner will taste!

First make the chermoula marinade. Put the sweet paprika, fresh and ground coriander, parsley, cumin, garlic, lime juice, red onion and cayenne pepper in a shallow ceramic dish. Season to taste and stir well.

Add the fish pieces to the marinade and turn to coat all over. Cover and chill for 4 hours or overnight if possible.

Preheat the grill to medium.

Thread the pepper pieces and fish chunks on to eight metal skewers (or wooden skewers soaked in water for 20 minutes to stop them burning). Arrange the skewers under the grill and cook for 3-4 minutes on each side or until the fish is just cooked through.

Scatter over the coriander and mint and serve hot with lime wedges, couscous and salad.

koshary

~egyptian rice, lentils and pasta~

serves 4

Free

Ⓥ

ready in 40 minutes

Having rice, lentils and pasta all in one dish may sound unusual but 80 million Egyptians can't be wrong! This satisfying combination from the land of the pharaohs is seriously tasty thanks to the stunning spices and sweet fried onions.

- low calorie cooking spray
- 2 onions, thinly sliced
- 2 garlic cloves, finely chopped
- 400g can chopped tomatoes
- 2 tbsp tomato purée
- 1 tsp dried red chilli flakes
- 150g Puy or brown lentils, rinsed and drained
- 2 tsp cumin seeds
- 1 tsp mustard seeds
- 1 tsp coriander seeds
- 1 cinnamon stick
- 200g basmati or long-grain rice, rinsed and drained
- 100g vermicelli pasta, broken into small pieces
- salt and freshly ground black pepper
- fresh coriander sprigs, to garnish

Spray a large non-stick frying pan with low calorie cooking spray and place over a medium heat. Add the onions and cook for 30 minutes or until deeply golden.

Meanwhile, put the garlic, tomatoes, tomato purée and dried chilli in a saucepan with 200ml of water and cook for 30 minutes over a medium-low heat, stirring often.

Put the lentils in another saucepan and cover generously with water. Bring to the boil and cook for 25 minutes or until tender. Drain well.

At the same time, lightly spray a wide non-stick saucepan with low calorie cooking spray and place over a medium heat. Add the spices, cook for a few seconds until fragrant then add the rice and vermicelli. Cook, stirring for a minute or so to coat, then add 600ml of water and season with a little salt. Bring to the boil over a high heat, cover tightly and cook for 12-15 minutes or until tender and the water has been absorbed.

Mix the rice and vermicelli mixture with the lentils and season with salt and pepper. Divide between warmed plates, spoon over the tomato sauce and fried onions and garnish with coriander sprigs to serve.

nectarine salad with mint and rosewater

serves 4

Free

Ⓥ

ready in 25 minutes, plus cooling and chilling

---

2 tbsp rosewater

1 tsp sweetener

finely grated zest of ½ unwaxed lime

8 ripe nectarines, halved, stoned and cut into wedges

fat free natural yogurt or fromage frais, sweetened to taste, to serve

small handful of shredded fresh mint, to decorate

The ripe nectarines, fresh mint and floral hints of the rosewater pack plenty of flavour into this completely Free dessert.

Put the rosewater and 200ml of water in a saucepan over a high heat. Bring to the boil then turn the heat to medium-low and simmer for 10 minutes to make a syrup. Add the sweetener and lime zest and leave to cool.

Put the nectarine wedges into a wide serving bowl and drizzle over the syrup. Toss to mix well, cover with cling film and chill for 2-3 hours or longer if time permits.

Divide the nectarine wedges and the juices between four chilled bowls, add a generous dollop of fat free natural yogurt or fromage frais and scatter over the mint to serve.

This dessert is equally delicious made with peaches instead of nectarines. Rosewater is available in larger supermarkets, specialist food shops and online but if you can't find any you can use 1 teaspoon of vanilla essence instead.

Italy

The cuisine of Italy is so popular around the world that we all speak a little bit of Italian now... even if it's just pasta, pizza, risotto and tiramisu! Their fabulous food is a Food Optimiser's dream because so much of it is filling, Free and packed with fantastic flavours.

bacon and vegetable spiedini

serves 4

Free

ready in 20 minutes

Spiedini are pieces of meat cooked on skewers and these tasty starters are loaded with fresh flavours and goodness.

- 8 mushrooms, quartered
- 1 large red onion, cut into wedges
- 1 courgette, sliced into thick rounds
- 16 back bacon rashers, visible fat removed
- salt and freshly ground black pepper
- 1 tbsp finely chopped fresh rosemary leaves
- low calorie cooking spray
- lemon wedges, to serve

Preheat the grill to medium-high.

Thread the vegetable pieces and bacon rashers alternately on to eight metal skewers (or wooden skewers that have been soaked in water for 20 minutes to stop them burning). Season to taste and sprinkle over the rosemary.

Spray the skewers with low calorie cooking spray and grill for 8-10 minutes, turning occasionally, or until the vegetables have softened and the bacon is crisp.

Remove from the heat and serve with lemon wedges to squeeze over.

pasta e fagioli

-pasta and beans-

serves 4

Free

⊛ Ⓥ

ready in 1 hour 40 minutes

---

1 onion, finely chopped

1 leek, sliced

2 carrots, peeled and diced

1 celery stick, diced

1 fennel bulb, diced

4 tomatoes, finely chopped

2 garlic cloves, crushed

1.5 litres boiling vegetable stock

200g dried small pasta shapes

2 x 400g cans cannellini beans, drained and rinsed

salt and freshly ground black pepper

small handful of finely chopped fresh parsley

This simple peasant soup of pasta and beans is great as a substantial starter or a satisfying lunch as it's warming, reviving and very filling! Italian migrants took it with them to the US, where it is widely known as 'pasta fazool'.

Put the onion, leek, carrots, celery, fennel, tomatoes, garlic and stock into a large saucepan and bring to the boil over a high heat. Reduce the heat to low and simmer for 1 hour.

Stir in the pasta and beans and cook for another 20-25 minutes or until the pasta is tender. Season to taste and stir in most of the parsley.

Ladle the soup into bowls and garnish with the remaining parsley to serve.

You can use canned borlotti beans instead of cannellini beans in this rustic soup – or use a can of each.

Capri

parma ham and melon salad

serves 4

1½ Syns per serving

ready in 20 minutes

Salty-sweet Parma ham, sun-ripened melons and peppery rocket leaves are an unforgettable combination in this classic starter.

1 cantaloupe melon

small bag of rocket leaves

8 thin Parma ham slices

for the dressing

1 red chilli, deseeded and finely chopped

1 tsp dried oregano

juice of 1 orange

Halve the melon and scoop out the seeds. Using a sharp knife, cut away the skin and slice the melon flesh into wedges.

Arrange the rocket leaves on four plates and divide the melon between them. Top each serving with two slices of Parma ham.

Mix the dressing ingredients and drizzle over the salad to serve.

vegetable antipasti

Griddling gives Mediterranean vegetables such as aubergines, courgettes and peppers a sensational smokiness. This beautiful platter is the perfect starter to share on a hot summer's day.

serves 4

Free

V SP

ready in 30 minutes

- 6 tbsp balsamic vinegar
- 3 garlic cloves, crushed
- 2 tsp dried basil
- 2 tsp dried oregano
- ½ tsp dried chilli flakes
- salt and freshly ground black pepper
- 200g baby courgettes, sliced thinly lengthways
- 2 aubergines, sliced thinly
- 2 red peppers, halved, deseeded and cut into thin strips
- 2 yellow peppers, halved, deseeded and cut into thin strips
- large bag of rocket leaves

Put the balsamic vinegar, garlic, basil, oregano and chilli flakes in a large bowl, season to taste and mix together. Add the courgettes, aubergines and peppers and toss to coat well.

Heat a non-stick griddle pan over a high heat.

Remove the vegetables from the balsamic marinade (reserving the marinade) and griddle, in batches, for 2-3 minutes on each side or until tender and nicely coloured.

Arrange the rocket leaves on a large serving platter, top with the grilled vegetables and drizzle over the reserved marinade.

These vegetables are delicious served warm or cold.

Make your Italian platter even more tempting by adding other nibbles such as light mozzarella cheese (3 Syns per 35g) or Parma ham (½ Syn per slice).

pollo alla cacciatora

-hunter's chicken-

serves 4

Free

❄

ready in 50 minutes

---

low calorie cooking spray

salt and freshly ground black pepper

8 skinless chicken thighs, visible fat removed

8 back bacon rashers, visible fat removed, roughly chopped

1 onion, roughly chopped

2 celery sticks, roughly chopped

2 garlic cloves, finely chopped

300g button mushrooms, halved

½ tsp dried red chilli flakes

1 red pepper, halved, deseeded and sliced

1 yellow pepper, halved, deseeded and sliced

500ml boiling chicken stock

2 bay leaves

250g passata

400g can cherry tomatoes

small handful of roughly chopped fresh parsley, to garnish

The story goes that this classic dish was originally prepared on hunting trips (or by the hunter's wife when he returned home). Tasty chicken thighs are cooked on the bone with plenty of fresh Mediterranean vegetables in a rich tomato sauce.

Spray a large non-stick frying pan with low calorie cooking spray and place over a high heat. Season the chicken pieces and cook for 5-6 minutes or until golden on both sides, turning regularly. Transfer the chicken to a wide casserole pan in a single layer and set aside.

Reduce the heat to medium and add the bacon to the frying pan. Cook for 2 minutes, stirring occasionally. Add the onion, celery, garlic, mushrooms, chilli and peppers and cook for 5 minutes or until the onion has softened. Add the stock and stir well.

Tip the mixture over the chicken in the casserole pan. Add the bay leaves, passata and the cherry tomatoes, along with the juices from the can, and bring to the boil. Reduce the heat to low, cover and simmer for 25-30 minutes or until cooked through, turning the chicken occasionally.

Season, scatter over the parsley and serve hot with your favourite potatoes.

piccata al limone
-turkey with lemon sauce-

This simple dish involves slicing and sautéing meat or poultry and serving it with a tangy lemon and caper sauce. It's traditionally made with veal, although we've used lean turkey breast steaks as they're much easier to find – and just as delicious!

serves 4

Free

ready in 30 minutes

---

8 turkey breast steaks, visible fat removed

salt and freshly ground black pepper

low calorie cooking spray

4 lemon slices, plus 1 tbsp lemon juice

250ml boiling chicken stock

2 tbsp bottled capers, drained and rinsed

small handful of finely chopped fresh parsley

Place the turkey steaks between sheets of cling film and pound to a 5mm thickness using a meat mallet or rolling pin. Season to taste.

Place a large non-stick frying pan over a high heat and spray with low calorie cooking spray. Add the turkey to the pan and cook in batches for 5 minutes on each side or until nicely browned, adding the lemon slices for the last 2 minutes.

Meanwhile, pour the chicken stock into a saucepan over a high heat and boil for 5-6 minutes. Stir in the capers, lemon juice and parsley.

Divide the turkey steaks between plates, garnish with the lemon slices and pour over the sauce. Serve hot with your favourite potatoes and vegetables.

pork meatballs in roasted vegetable sauce

serves 4

Free

❄

ready in 1 hour

Italy is famous for meatballs and this easy recipe pairs pleasing nuggets of pork with a tempting roasted vegetable sauce. They're Free and very filling!

500g lean pork mince (5% fat or less)

2 tsp dried thyme

small handful of roughly chopped fresh parsley, to garnish

for the vegetable sauce

2 courgettes, cut into chunks

2 red peppers, halved, deseeded and cut into chunks

2 red onions, cut into wedges

2 garlic cloves, halved

low calorie cooking spray

salt and freshly ground black pepper

400g can chopped tomatoes

4 tbsp tomato purée

1 tsp sweetener

Preheat the oven to 200°C/Fan 180°C/Gas 6.

First roast the vegetables to make the sauce. Put the courgettes, peppers, onions and garlic into a roasting tin and spray with low calorie cooking spray. Season to taste and roast for 30 minutes, turning occasionally.

Meanwhile, put the pork in a bowl with the dried thyme. Season well and, using your hands, shape the mixture into 24 meatballs. Chill them while the vegetables roast.

Put the roasted vegetables in a food processor with the chopped tomatoes, tomato purée, sweetener and 150ml of water. Blitz until smooth and check the seasoning.

Pour the sauce into the same roasting tin you used for the vegetables and drop in the meatballs (without stirring them in yet). Roast for 20 minutes then stir the meatballs into the sauce.

Garnish the meatballs with parsley and serve them hot with pasta or rice.

creamy mushroom and broad bean carbonara

serves 4
Free
ready in 30 minutes

The classic creamy bacon pasta dish is a joy to eat and so easy to make. We've added mushrooms and podded broad beans for extra goodness.

500g dried spaghetti or other long pasta

250g broad beans, podded

low calorie cooking spray

8 back bacon rashers, visible fat removed, roughly chopped

2 garlic cloves, finely chopped

250g chestnut mushrooms, sliced

3 large egg yolks*

100g quark

salt and freshly ground black pepper

**Pregnant women, the elderly and babies are advised not to eat raw or partially cooked eggs.*

Cook the pasta according to the packet instructions, adding the broad beans for the last 2 minutes of the cooking time. Drain, reserving a few tablespoons of the cooking water.

Meanwhile, spray a non-stick frying pan with low calorie cooking spray and place over a high heat. Add the bacon and cook for 3-4 minutes, then add the garlic and mushrooms and cook for another 4 minutes.

In a small bowl, whisk the egg yolks and quark with some seasoning.

Add the bacon mixture to the drained pasta and stir through. Stir in the egg and quark mixture, adding 2-3 tablespoons of the reserved cooking water to loosen the sauce a little if necessary. The residual heat will cook the eggs just enough to thicken the sauce.

This is best served hot and is delicious with a mixed salad.

tagliata

-sliced beef salad-

In this more-ish main course, juicy steak is cut thinly, tossed with potatoes and tomatoes and served in a punchy dressing. The name comes from the Italian word tagliare, meaning 'to cut'.

serves 4

Free

ready in 20 minutes

200g cherry tomatoes

low calorie cooking spray

salt and freshly ground black pepper

1kg new or baby potatoes, halved

4 x 250g lean beef fillet or sirloin steaks, visible fat removed

½ tsp mustard powder

4 tsp balsamic vinegar

100ml fat free vinaigrette

small bag of rocket leaves

Preheat the oven to 180°C/Fan 160°C/Gas 4.

Put the cherry tomatoes into a non-stick roasting tin, spray with low calorie cooking spray and season to taste. Roast in the oven for 15 minutes or until the tomatoes are just tender.

Meanwhile, cook the potatoes in lightly salted boiling water for 12-15 minutes. Drain and keep warm.

Heat a non-stick griddle or frying pan over a high heat until smoking hot. Spray the steaks on both sides with low calorie cooking spray, season to taste and fry them just how you like them (2 minutes on each side for rare, 3 minutes on each side for medium or 4 minutes on each side for well done). Remove the steaks from the heat and rest for a few minutes then cut each one into thin slices.

Mix the mustard powder and balsamic vinegar in a small bowl, then whisk in the vinaigrette and season to taste.

Divide the rocket leaves, tomatoes, potatoes and steak between four plates. Pour over the dressing, toss well and serve hot, with an extra grind of black pepper.

tagliatelle bolognese

The classic beefy sauce from Bologna has become a favourite all over the world! While we Brits usually serve it with spaghetti, Italians favour other types of pasta that hold the sauce better such as tagliatelle – but whatever kind you use it'll be sensational!

serves 4

Free

❄ (sauce only)

ready in 40 minutes

---

low calorie cooking spray

500g lean beef mince (5% fat or less)

1 onion, finely chopped

2 carrots, peeled and diced

1 courgette, diced

150g closed-cup mushrooms, diced

2 garlic cloves, finely chopped

2 x 400g cans chopped tomatoes

small handful of torn fresh basil leaves, plus whole leaves to garnish

1 beef stock cube

salt and freshly ground black pepper

500g dried long pasta, such as tagliatelle or spaghetti

Spray a non-stick frying pan with low calorie cooking spray and place over a medium-high heat. Add the mince and stir-fry for 4-5 minutes, then add the onion, carrots, courgette, mushrooms and garlic and stir-fry for a further 3-4 minutes.

Add the tomatoes and basil, crumble in the stock cube, season and stir. Bring to the boil then reduce the heat to low, cover and simmer for 15 minutes, stirring occasionally. Remove the lid and cook for a further 5 minutes.

Meanwhile, cook the pasta according to the packet instructions and drain.

Divide the pasta between shallow bowls and spoon over the bolognese sauce. Garnish with a few whole basil leaves, give each bowl a good grind of black pepper and serve nice and hot.

For a delicious variation, use a mix of lean beef and pork mince (5% fat or less).

seafood risotto

serves 4

Free

ready in 45 minutes

Italy is blessed with a very long coastline and Italians make full use of their fish and seafood in all sorts of irresistible dishes. In this one, filling risotto rice takes on the fantastic flavour of fresh fish.

- low calorie cooking spray
- 1 onion, finely chopped
- 2 garlic cloves, finely chopped
- 1 fennel bulb, trimmed and finely chopped
- 300g dried risotto rice
- 1.5 litres boiling fish stock
- 175g raw king or tiger prawns
- 2 white fish fillets, cut into bite-sized chunks
- 1 salmon fillet, cut into bite-sized chunks
- salt and freshly ground black pepper
- bunch of spring onions, trimmed and finely sliced
- small handful of finely chopped fresh chives

Spray a wide, heavy-based saucepan with low calorie cooking spray and place over a medium heat. Add the onion, garlic and fennel and cook for 3-4 minutes or until starting to soften. Add the rice and stir to mix well.

Add 1 ladleful of stock to the pan and stir occasionally to make sure the rice doesn't stick to the pan. When most of the liquid is absorbed, add another ladleful of stock and repeat until all the stock is absorbed and the risotto is nice and creamy.

When the risotto is nearly cooked (this will take about 20-25 minutes), add the prawns and fish, stir well and cook for 10 minutes. Season to taste and remove from the heat.

Scatter over the spring onions and chives and serve hot in shallow bowls.

tuna and bean salad

This tasty Free salad is packed with great ingredients competing for your fork's attention! Using cans of tuna and beans makes it so easy to prepare.

serves 4

Free

ready in 20 minutes

200g green beans

200g sugar snap peas

2 x 185g cans tuna steak in spring water or brine, drained and flaked

2 x 410g cans mixed beans, drained and rinsed

1 red onion, finely chopped

1 red chilli, deseeded and roughly chopped

2 tomatoes, roughly chopped

1 Little Gem lettuce

zest of ½ unwaxed lemon, to garnish

for the dressing

6 tbsp fat free vinaigrette

2 garlic cloves, crushed

½ tsp mustard powder

salt and freshly ground black pepper

Bring a large pan of lightly salted water to the boil and add the green beans and sugar snap peas. Bring back to the boil then drain and refresh under cold running water. Drain again and put the green beans and sugar snap peas into a mixing bowl.

Add the tuna, canned beans, onion, chilli and tomatoes to the mixing bowl and stir well.

Arrange the lettuce leaves in a serving dish and tip the tuna and bean mix over the top.

Mix all the dressing ingredients in a bowl, season to taste and pour over the tuna mixture. Toss thoroughly and scatter over the lemon zest to serve.

herbed gnocchi in tomato sauce

serves 4

Free

ready in 50 minutes, plus chilling

Gnocchi are filling potato dumplings that go brilliantly with so many sauces. Here we've served them with a classic tomato sauce that the whole family will enjoy.

- 800g potatoes, peeled and cut into chunks
- 2 large handfuls of finely chopped fresh herbs, such as chives, parsley and chervil
- a little freshly grated nutmeg
- 1 egg, beaten

for the tomato sauce

- 2 x 400g cans chopped tomatoes
- 1 onion, finely chopped
- 3 garlic cloves, crushed
- small handful of finely chopped fresh basil
- salt and freshly ground black pepper

Cook the potatoes in a saucepan of lightly salted boiling water for 12-15 minutes then drain well.

Add the herbs, nutmeg and egg to the potatoes and mash well. Cool, cover and chill for 30 minutes or overnight if you have time.

When you're ready to cook, preheat the oven to 190°C/Fan 170°C/Gas 5.

Make the sauce by putting the tomatoes, onion, garlic and basil in a saucepan over a high heat. Season to taste and bring to the boil then turn the heat down to medium and cook for 6-8 minutes. Spread the mixture over the base of a shallow ovenproof dish.

Shape the potato mixture into bite-sized balls and arrange them in a single layer on top of the tomato mixture. Grind over a little black pepper and bake in the oven for 20 minutes or until hot and bubbling.

These are amazing served hot with salad.

For a cheesy treat, sprinkle freshly grated Parmesan (or a vegetarian alternative) over the gnocchi and put them under a medium grill for the last 5 minutes of the cooking time (2 level tablespoons adds ½ Syn per serving).

vegetable lasagne

You don't need meat to make a lasagne magnificent and the colours in this vegetable version make it a feast for the eyes too.

serves 4

Free

Ⓥ

ready in 1 hour 10 minutes

- 1 red pepper, halved, deseeded and cut into chunks
- 1 yellow pepper, halved, deseeded and cut into chunks
- 1 red onion, roughly chopped
- 2 courgettes, thickly sliced
- 1 aubergine, cubed
- 1 garlic clove, crushed
- 1 tbsp mixed dried herbs
- salt and freshly ground black pepper
- low calorie cooking spray
- 500g passata
- 10 dried lasagne sheets
- 1 tbsp finely chopped fresh parsley

for the white sauce

- 300g fat free natural Greek yogurt
- 3 eggs
- a little freshly grated nutmeg

Preheat the oven to 200°C/Fan 180°C/Gas 6.

Put the peppers, onion, courgettes, aubergine and garlic in a roasting tin. Sprinkle with the mixed herbs, season to taste and spray with low calorie cooking spray. Roast for 20 minutes or until the vegetables are just tender and starting to char around the edges. Remove from the oven and stir in the passata.

Meanwhile, make the white sauce. Put the yogurt, eggs and nutmeg in a bowl, season to taste and mix well.

Turn the oven down to 190°C/Fan 170°C/Gas 5.

Arrange half the roasted vegetables in an ovenproof dish, cover with half of the lasagne sheets – breaking them up to fit if necessary – and spread half of the white sauce over the top. Repeat to use up the remaining ingredients, finishing with the white sauce, and bake for 25 minutes or until golden.

Scatter over the parsley and serve hot with salad.

For a meaty lasagne, make up our classic bolognese (page 137) and use half of the recipe in place of the roasted vegetables.

risi e bisi
-rice and peas-

serves 4
Free
V
ready in 35 minutes

1 onion, finely chopped
2 carrots, peeled and diced
1 celery stick, diced
2 garlic cloves, finely chopped
1.5 litres boiling vegetable stock
300g dried risotto rice
300g frozen peas
small handful of finely chopped fresh parsley
salt and freshly ground black pepper

This traditional dish is slightly 'wetter' than a risotto but just as easy to prepare and comforting to eat.

Put the onion, carrots, celery and garlic in a heavy-based saucepan and place over a high heat. Add the stock and rice and bring to the boil. Turn the heat to low and simmer gently for 15-20 minutes, stirring once or twice.

Stir in the peas and cook for a further 5 minutes or until the peas are tender.

Stir in the parsley, season to taste and ladle into bowls to serve.

Freshly grated Parmesan (or a vegetarian alternative) is a tasty addition to this simple dish (2 level tablespoons adds ½ Syn per serving).

HOTEL LUNA

baked spinach cannelloni

Cannelloni are large pasta tubes that can be filled with all sorts of sensational ingredients, smothered in sauce and baked for a simple yet impressive dinner.

serves 4

Free

Ⓥ

ready in 1 hour

low calorie cooking spray

2 large bags of spinach, washed and trimmed

750g low fat natural cottage cheese

½ tsp dried red chilli flakes

a little freshly grated nutmeg

2 egg yolks

salt and freshly ground black pepper

500g dried cannelloni tubes

small handful of torn fresh basil leaves, to garnish

for the tomato sauce

1kg passata

1 tsp dried oregano

1 tbsp sweetener

2 garlic cloves, crushed

Preheat the oven to 200°C/Fan 180°C/Gas 6 and spray a 30 x 20cm ovenproof dish with low calorie cooking spray.

First make the filling. Put the spinach in a saucepan with 2 tablespoons of water. Cover with a lid and cook very gently over a low heat for 5 minutes or until the leaves are limp. Drain in a colander, pressing down on the spinach to squeeze out any excess liquid.

Put the spinach into a food processor with the cottage cheese, chilli, nutmeg and egg yolks. Season to taste and blitz until smooth, then use the mixture to fill the cannelloni tubes (using a piping bag is the easiest way to do this). Arrange the cannelloni tubes in the prepared ovenproof dish.

Make the tomato sauce by mixing the passata, oregano, sweetener and garlic in a bowl. Season to taste and pour over the cannelloni. Cover with foil and bake for 20-25 minutes, then remove the foil and bake for a further 20 minutes or until bubbling.

Scatter over the basil and divide between plates. This is fantastic served hot with salad.

For extra flavour and a golden topping, sprinkle 2 level tablespoons of freshly grated Parmesan (or a vegetarian alternative) over the cannelloni before baking (½ Syn per serving).

margherita pizza

serves 4

7½ Syns per serving

❄ Ⓥ

ready in 1 hour

125g strong bread flour

7g sachet instant active yeast

1 tsp salt

for the topping

4 shallots, finely chopped

3 garlic cloves, crushed

1 tsp dried red chilli flakes

2 tsp dried oregano

400g can chopped tomatoes

1 tbsp tomato purée

salt and freshly ground black pepper

70g light mozzarella cheese, cubed or sliced

small handful of torn fresh basil leaves, to garnish

Britain's favourite Italian export is a doddle to make at home! Rolling out your own dough is great fun and our lighter recipe keeps the Syns down to just 7½ Syns per serving!

Put all the topping ingredients apart from the mozzarella into a saucepan, season to taste and cook over a medium-low heat for 25-30 minutes or until you have a thick, spreadable sauce.

Meanwhile, preheat the oven to 200°C/Fan 180°C/Gas 6 and put in a baking sheet or, better still, a pizza stone to heat through – this will help your pizza cook evenly.

Put the flour into a large bowl and stir in the yeast and salt. Make a well in the middle, pour in 75ml of warm water and mix with a wooden spoon until you have soft, fairly wet dough. Dust a surface very lightly with flour (1 level teaspoon is ½ Syn), turn out the dough and knead for 5 minutes until smooth. Use a rolling pin to roll the dough into a thin circle about 22cm across.

Put your rolled-out base on to the preheated pizza stone or baking sheet (add a sheet of non-stick baking parchment if using a baking sheet). Spoon the tomato sauce over the base and arrange the mozzarella on top.

Bake for 15-20 minutes or until the base is golden. Scatter over the basil and serve hot with a rocket salad.

If you're feeling creative, feel free to add other ingredients too. Peppers, mushrooms, lean ham and skinless cooked chicken are all Free – or try a Fiorentina-style pizza using spinach and an egg cracked on top.

penne arrabiata

Arrabiata means angry and this satisfying storecupboard favourite is so-called because of the heat of the chilli. Perfect for putting together pronto when time is short!

serves 4

Free

(sauce only)

ready in 20 minutes

- half a bunch of spring onions, finely chopped
- 3 garlic cloves, crushed
- 1 red chilli, deseeded and finely chopped
- 1 tsp dried red chilli flakes
- 2 tsp dried oregano
- 400g can chopped tomatoes
- 100ml boiling vegetable stock or water
- salt and freshly ground black pepper
- 500g dried penne or other pasta shapes
- small handful of fresh basil leaves, to garnish

Put the spring onions, garlic, fresh and dried chilli, oregano, tomatoes and stock into a saucepan over a high heat and bring to the boil. Reduce the heat to low, season to taste and cook gently for 10-12 minutes.

While the sauce is cooking, cook the pasta according to the packet instructions and drain well.

Mix the sauce into the pasta and divide between plates or bowls. Scatter over the basil leaves, grind over plenty of black pepper and serve hot.

A scattering of freshly grated Parmesan (or a vegetarian alternative) takes this simple pasta dish to another level (2 level tablespoons adds ½ Syn per serving). Pitted black olives are another great addition: add eight sliced olives to the pan along with the tomatoes and chilli (½ Syn per serving).

strawberry chocolate tiramisu

serves 4

2 Syns per serving

ready in 15 minutes, plus chilling

- 4 sponge fingers, broken into small pieces
- 150ml coffee, cooled
- 4 tbsp quark
- 2 tbsp sweetener
- 1 tsp vanilla extract
- 2 x 175g pots Muller Light Vanilla yogurt (or any Free vanilla yogurt)
- 400g strawberries, hulled and halved
- 15g dark chocolate

Tuck into our tantalising tiramisu for a dreamy taste of la dolce vita, with fresh strawberries to add a fruity twist.

Put the sponge fingers in a bowl and pour over the coffee. Divide this mixture between four dessert glasses.

Mix together the quark, sweetener, vanilla extract and yogurts in a bowl, then spoon half the mixture into the glasses.

Add the strawberries and the remaining quark mixture to the glasses, then cover and chill for 2-3 hours.

Grate the chocolate on top when you're ready to serve.

vanilla panna cotta

serves 4

Free

ready in 15 minutes, plus cooling and chilling

Panna cotta means 'cooked cream' and this indulgent dessert is traditionally made with lots of cream, milk and sugar. Our lighter version is every bit as delightful and amazingly it's completely Free!

- 200g quark
- 4 tbsp sweetener
- 1 tsp vanilla extract
- 2 x 175g pots Muller Light Vanilla yogurt (or any Free vanilla yogurt)
- 12g gelatine sachet
- 1 egg white*
- vanilla pods and mint sprigs, to decorate (optional)

**Pregnant women, the elderly and babies are advised not to eat raw or partially cooked eggs.*

Whisk the quark, sweetener, vanilla extract and yogurts in a bowl until smooth.

Place 2 tablespoons of hot water in a small heatproof bowl and sprinkle with gelatine. Stand the bowl in a saucepan of hot water and stir until the gelatine has dissolved. Allow to cool for about 5 minutes then whisk into the yogurt mixture.

Beat the egg white until soft peaks form then gently fold the egg white through the yogurt. Spoon the mixture into four individual moulds and chill in the fridge for 3 hours or until set.

When you're ready to eat, dip the moulds in a bowl of hot water for a few seconds and turn out on to plates. Decorate with vanilla pods and mint sprigs (if using) to serve.

semifreddo with raspberry coulis

serves 8

2½ Syns per serving

ready in 25 minutes, plus freezing

350g low fat custard from a can or carton

150g fat free natural fromage frais

1 tsp vanilla extract

2-3 tbsp sweetener

3 egg whites*

for the coulis

250g raspberries

½ tsp sweetener

**Pregnant women, the elderly and babies are advised not to eat raw or partially cooked eggs.*

Semifreddo means half-cold and this wonderful frozen custard pudding is a lighter alternative to ice cream. The fruit coulis adds an extra layer of sweetness that will thrill your tastebuds.

Put the custard and fromage frais in a large mixing bowl. Add the vanilla extract and sweetener and stir to mix well.

Whisk the egg whites in another bowl until stiff peaks form then gently fold into the custard mixture using a metal spoon.

Line a medium-sized loaf tin with cling film. Spoon the mixture into the tin, cover with cling film and firm up in the freezer for 6 hours or overnight if time permits.

Make the coulis by putting 200g of the raspberries and the sweetener in a food processor and blitzing until smooth. Chill the coulis until it's needed.

About 20 minutes before serving, transfer the semifreddo from the freezer to the fridge to soften slightly.

Spoon the coulis around serving plates. Turn out the semifreddo on to a board, cut into slices and place a slice on each plate.

Scatter over the remaining raspberries to serve.

lemon and honey granita

serves 8

½ **Syn** per serving

ready in 15 minutes, plus freezing

Granitas are desserts made from flavoured ice crystals and they were first made on the Italian island of Sicily. This zesty version is amazingly light and refreshing – it's the perfect way to round off a meal.

4 tbsp sweetener

5 unwaxed lemons

2 level tbsp runny honey

Put the sweetener and 400ml of water into a saucepan and bring to a simmer over a medium heat. Pare the zest from 1 lemon and add most of it to the pan, keeping a little back to decorate. Heat until the sweetener has dissolved, stirring occasionally. Bring to the boil then remove from the heat and leave to cool. When the syrup is cold, strain it into a large shallow plastic container.

Halve the remaining lemons lengthways and juice them, reserving the shells (slice off a tiny bit so that the lemon halves can sit upright like a bowl). Stir the lemon juice into the syrup along with the honey.

Freeze for 2 hours then remove from the freezer and, using a fork, mash up any ice crystals that have formed.

Return to the freezer for another 2 hours and mash the ice crystals again. Freeze for at least another 1 hour before spooning into the reserved lemon shells. Decorate with the reserved zest to serve.

Greece

Fresh veg, filling beans and tasty meats and cheeses make the food of Greece rich, satisfying and full of goodness. Dive into favourites like indulgent moussaka, refreshing Greek salad or sensational spanakopita.

mushrooms à la grecque

serves 4

½ **Syn** per serving

Ⓥ

ready in 25 minutes, plus standing

low calorie cooking spray

2 large onions, finely sliced

4 garlic cloves, crushed

600g baby button mushrooms, halved

8 tomatoes, roughly chopped

8 pitted black olives, sliced

2 tbsp white wine vinegar

salt and freshly ground black pepper

small handful of shredded fresh oregano leaves, plus sprigs to garnish

This more-ish mushroom salad is so easy to make and full of flavour. Serve it as a sensational starter or side dish with grilled fish, meat or chicken.

Spray a large, non-stick frying pan with low calorie cooking spray and fry the onions and half the garlic for about 10 minutes or until they are soft and starting to brown. Add the mushrooms and tomatoes and gently stir-fry for 5 minutes. Transfer the mixture to a serving dish and stir in the olives.

Mix the remaining garlic with the vinegar, season and drizzle over the mushrooms. Cover and stand for 30 minutes or chill overnight if time permits.

Scatter over the chopped oregano and garnish with the oregano sprigs to serve.

spiced feta fritters with tzatziki

serves 4 (makes 16)

2 Syns per serving

V

ready in 30 minutes, plus chilling

---

large bag of baby spinach leaves

2 courgettes, coarsely grated

50g reduced fat feta cheese, crumbled

2 tsp cumin seeds

small handful of finely chopped fresh dill

1 red chilli, deseeded and finely chopped

2 eggs, lightly beaten

2 level tbsp self-raising flour

low calorie cooking spray

lemon wedges, to serve

for the tzatziki

½ cucumber, cubed, plus extra finely chopped cucumber, to garnish

1 garlic clove, crushed

500g fat free natural Greek yogurt

2 tsp dried mint

salt and freshly ground black pepper

These irresistible golden bites are packed with fresh veg and creamy feta, while the tzatziki dip is the perfect partner.

First mix all the tzatziki ingredients in a bowl. Season with salt and chill until you're ready to serve.

Put the spinach and 1 tablespoon of water into a saucepan over a low heat. Cover with a lid and cook gently for 5 minutes or until the leaves are limp. Drain in a colander, pressing down on the spinach to squeeze out any excess liquid. Roughly chop and tip into a mixing bowl.

Put the courgette into a fine sieve and, using the back of a spoon, squeeze out as much liquid as you can. Add to the spinach along with the feta, cumin seeds, dill, chilli, eggs and flour. Season, mix well and divide the mixture into 16 equal portions. Using your hands, shape each portion into a fritter and set aside on a piece of non-stick baking parchment.

Spray a large non-stick frying pan with low calorie cooking spray and place over a medium-high heat. Cook the fritters in batches for 2-3 minutes each side or until golden and just cooked through.

Scatter the extra cucumber over the tzatziki, grind over a little black pepper and serve with the fritters and lemon wedges to squeeze over.

avgolemono
~egg and lemon soup~

serves 4

Free

Ⓥ

ready in 30 minutes

This warming soup is thickened with eggs and infused with the zesty freshness of lemon juice, with orzo pasta making it great as a tasty starter or light lunch.

1.5 litres vegetable stock

200g dried orzo pasta

thickly pared zest and juice of 1 large lemon

4 cardamom pods

2 bay leaves

2 cloves

salt and freshly ground black pepper

2 eggs, plus 2 extra yolks*

half a bunch of finely chopped spring onions

small handful of finely chopped fresh dill, plus a few sprigs to garnish

**Pregnant women, the elderly and babies are advised not to eat raw or partially cooked eggs.*

Put the stock in a large saucepan over a high heat and bring to the boil. Add the orzo, lemon zest, cardamom, bay leaves and cloves and season with salt and freshly ground black pepper. Reduce the heat to medium and simmer until the orzo is tender – this will take about 12-15 minutes.

Remove and discard the lemon zest, cardamom, bay leaves and cloves. Bring the stock and orzo back to the boil over a high heat, then reduce the heat to low.

Whisk the whole eggs, yolks and lemon juice in a large bowl until well combined.

Ladle about 500ml of the hot stock into the eggs and slowly whisk it in, then slowly whisk the egg mixture back into the soup.

Continue to cook the soup over a low heat, stirring constantly until slightly thickened – this will take about 5 minutes.

Stir in the spring onions and divide the soup between bowls. Scatter over the dill, grind over a little more pepper and serve hot.

If you can't get hold of orzo, use tiny dried pasta shapes, such as conchigliette.

greek salad with watermelon

serves 4

3½ Syns per serving

Ⓥ

ready in 15 minutes

---

4 tomatoes, cut into wedges

1 cucumber, deseeded and roughly chopped

1 red onion, roughly chopped

2 green peppers, deseeded and roughly chopped

300g watermelon flesh, deseeded and cut into bite-sized chunks

150g reduced fat feta cheese, cut into chunks

small handful of finely chopped fresh parsley

salt and freshly ground black pepper

for the dressing

juice of 1 lemon, plus wedges to serve

1 tsp dried oregano

A good Greek salad is so refreshing when the weather is hot. Crunchy peppers, creamy feta and sweet, juicy tomatoes capture the best of the Mediterranean on a plate, and we've added watermelon for an extra burst of freshness!

Put the tomatoes, cucumber, onion, peppers, watermelon and feta into a wide salad bowl. Scatter over the parsley and season to taste.

Mix together the lemon juice and oregano. Drizzle over the salad, toss to combine and serve with lemon wedges to squeeze over.

stifado
-greek beef stew-

serves 4

Free

❄

ready in 3 hours

2 onions, finely sliced

3 garlic cloves, crushed

750ml boiling beef stock

500g lean beef steak, visible fat removed, cut into chunks

1 tbsp tomato purée

2 tbsp red wine vinegar

1 tbsp fresh thyme leaves

1 tbsp chopped fresh rosemary leaves

1 bay leaf

2 tsp cumin seeds

½ tsp ground cloves

1 cinnamon stick

200g shallots, peeled

juice of ½ lemon

salt and freshly ground black pepper

small handful of finely chopped fresh coriander

This aromatic stew of beef and vegetables shows off Greek slow-cooking at its best: just let your cooker do all the work for you.

Put the onions, garlic and 300ml of stock in a large casserole pan, cover and bring to the boil over a high heat. Boil for 5-10 minutes then reduce the heat to low and simmer uncovered for 20-30 minutes or until the onions are tender and golden.

Preheat the oven to 160°C/Fan 140°C/Gas 3.

Add the beef to the casserole pan and cook over a low heat until browned all over, turning occasionally. Stir in the tomato purée, vinegar, herbs and spices, along with the remaining stock. Cover and bring to the boil, then transfer to the oven and cook for 2-2½ hours.

About 1 hour before the end of cooking, blanch the shallots in boiling water for 1 minute then drain and add to the casserole.

To serve, add the lemon juice, season to taste and scatter with coriander. This is great with orzo or your favourite short-shaped pasta.

yemista
-beef-stuffed tomatoes-

The Greeks love to stuff vegetables and giant tomatoes are a particular favourite! We've used lean beef mince to keep them Free!

serves 4

Free

ready in 1 hour 30 minutes

- low calorie cooking spray
- 2 onions, finely chopped
- 4 garlic cloves, crushed
- 500g lean beef mince (5% fat or less)
- 2 tsp dried oregano
- 1 tsp ground cinnamon
- 125g tomato purée
- 100g dried long-grain rice
- 300ml boiling vegetable stock
- small handful of finely chopped fresh mint
- small handful of finely chopped fresh dill, plus extra to garnish
- salt and freshly ground black pepper
- 4 giant tomatoes (or use 8 large tomatoes)

Spray a large non-stick frying pan with low calorie cooking spray and place over a low heat. Add the onions and garlic and cook gently for 12-15 minutes or until softened.

Add the beef, oregano, cinnamon and tomato purée, turn the heat up to medium and stir-fry for 6-8 minutes or until the meat is browned. Drain off any excess liquid or fat.

Stir in the rice and stock and turn the heat to high. Bring to the boil, then turn the heat to low and simmer gently for 20-25 minutes or until the rice is tender and the stock has been absorbed. Stir in the fresh herbs and season to taste.

Meanwhile, preheat the oven to 200°C/Fan 180°C/Gas 6.

Slice off and set aside the tops of the tomatoes. Scoop out and discard most of the seeds and pulp with a teaspoon, being careful not to break the skin. Place the hollowed-out tomatoes cut side up in a baking tin.

Spoon the beef mixture into the tomatoes and place the tomato lids back on top. Bake for 25-30 minutes or until the tomatoes have softened and are just starting to collapse.

Garnish the tomatoes with the extra dill and serve them hot with salad.

If you have any of the beef mixture left over, it makes a great topping for jacket potatoes.

moussaka

serves 4
Free
ready in 1 hour 30 minutes

Our version of the classic lamb and aubergine bake takes out all of the oil and Syns while keeping all of the flavour and goodness!

- low calorie cooking spray
- 2 aubergines, thinly sliced
- 2 onions, chopped
- 500g lean lamb leg steaks, visible fat removed, roughly chopped
- 400g can chopped tomatoes
- 1 tbsp chopped fresh oregano (or 1 tsp dried)
- ½ teaspoon ground cinnamon
- ½ teaspoon allspice
- ½ teaspoon cumin
- 2 tbsp tomato purée
- 4 tbsp lamb or vegetable stock
- salt and freshly ground black pepper

for the topping

- 300g fat free natural Greek yogurt
- 3 eggs, beaten
- a little freshly grated nutmeg
- 1 tsp dried mint

Spray a non-stick frying pan with low calorie cooking spray and place over a medium heat. Add the aubergines in batches and fry until slightly coloured. Transfer to a plate and set aside.

Add the onions to the pan and cook gently until softened and translucent, then add the lamb, tomatoes, oregano, spices and tomato purée. Turn the heat to high, bring to the boil and cook rapidly until the sauce thickens. Stir in the stock, season to taste and cook for 3 minutes.

Preheat the oven to 180°C/Fan 160°C/Gas 4.

Arrange half of the aubergine slices in a shallow ovenproof dish. Cover with the meat sauce and finish off with another layer of the aubergines.

Beat the topping ingredients together, season well and pour over the aubergine. Bake for 30 minutes or until the topping is set, golden and slightly risen.

Serve hot with plenty of salad.

pork souvlaki

serves 4
Free
SP
ready in 25 minutes, plus marinating

The distinctively Greek marinade of oregano, mint, lemon and garlic makes these tempting pork skewers unforgettable – leave them to marinate overnight for maximum flavour!

- finely grated zest and juice of 3 unwaxed lemons
- 2 tbsp dried oregano
- 2 tbsp dried mint
- 3 garlic cloves, crushed
- 500g lean pork fillet, visible fat removed, cut into chunks
- salt and freshly ground black pepper
- 2 onions, cut into wedges
- 1 red pepper, halved, deseeded and cut into large chunks
- 1 yellow pepper, halved, deseeded and cut into large chunks
- small handful of finely chopped fresh basil or Greek basil leaves, to garnish

Mix the lemon zest and juice, oregano, mint and garlic in a shallow bowl. Add the pork, season to taste and mix together. Marinate in the fridge for 4 hours or overnight if time permits.

Preheat the grill to medium-hot.

Thread the pork, onion wedges and pepper pieces on to eight metal skewers (or wooden skewers soaked in water for 20 minutes to stop them burning). Grill the kebabs for 5-6 minutes on each side or until cooked through.

Scatter over the basil and serve hot with plenty of salad.

baked cod stew with crispy potatoes

serves 4

Free

❄

ready in 2 hours

---

low calorie cooking spray

2 onions, chopped

1 red chilli, deseeded and finely chopped

2 garlic cloves, finely chopped

1 yellow pepper, halved, deseeded and roughly chopped

2 red peppers, halved, deseeded and roughly chopped

2 bay leaves

8 potatoes, peeled and thinly sliced

2 carrots, peeled and finely sliced

4 skinless cod fillets or other white fish, cut into bite-sized chunks

100g tomato purée

300ml boiling vegetable stock

small handful of roughly chopped fresh parsley

Enjoying the fresh seafood landed by local fishermen is one of the highlights of eating out in Greece. We've used cod for this satisfying stew although you could use whatever fish you have in the fridge.

Preheat the oven to 150°C/Fan 130°C/Gas 2.

Spray a large non-stick saucepan with low calorie cooking spray and place over a medium heat. Add the onions and stir-fry for 10-12 minutes or until they start to soften.

Add the chilli to the pan and cook for 2-3 minutes then stir in the garlic, peppers and bay leaves and cook for 1 minute.

Lightly spray a deep ovenproof dish with low calorie cooking spray and cover the base with half of the potatoes. Add the carrots and then the cod, finishing with a layer of potatoes. Mix the tomato purée and stock, pour over the fish and vegetables and cover with foil. Bake for 1 hour 20 minutes then uncover the dish and cook for a further 15 minutes or until the fish is cooked through and the potatoes and vegetables are tender.

Scatter over the parsley and serve hot with your favourite vegetables.

soupies

-squid stew-

This super-tasty meal brings out all the fabulous flavour of squid without the sky-high Syns you get with deep-fried kalamari.

serves 4

Free

ready in 1 hour 20 minutes

- low calorie cooking spray
- 900g prepared fresh squid, cleaned and sliced into thick rings (or use 3 x 300g packs frozen squid rings, thawed)
- 2 onions, finely chopped
- 2 bay leaves
- 5 cloves
- 1 cinnamon stick
- 500g passata with onions and garlic
- 300ml boiling vegetable stock
- 3 garlic cloves, crushed
- juice of 1 lemon
- 1 tsp paprika
- 1 tsp dried oregano
- salt and freshly ground black pepper
- fresh oregano leaves, to garnish

Lightly spray a wide non-stick saucepan with low calorie cooking spray and place over a low heat. Add the squid, onions, bay leaves, cloves and cinnamon stick then cover and simmer for 10-12 minutes or until the squid has released its juices.

Uncover the pan and simmer until the juice has mostly evaporated. Remove and discard the bay leaves, cloves and cinnamon stick.

Stir in the passata, stock, garlic, lemon juice, paprika and dried oregano. Season to taste, cover and cook over a low heat for 1 hour, stirring occasionally. Remove the lid 10 minutes before the end of the cooking time to allow the stew to thicken a little.

Ladle the stew into bowls, garnish with oregano leaves and serve with your favourite vegetables.

Frozen squid rings cook faster so if you're using them, it's worth checking to see if they're done after 45 minutes.

spanakopita

~spinach and feta pie~

Spinach and feta is a classic combination in Greek cooking and this indulgent pie will show you why! Slice through the crispy filo pastry and discover some truly amazing taste sensations.

serves 4

5½ Syns per serving

Ⓥ

ready in 1 hour

1kg frozen spinach

bunch of finely chopped spring onions

small handful of finely chopped fresh parsley

small handful of finely chopped fresh dill

100g reduced fat feta cheese, crumbled

250g low fat natural cottage cheese

2 garlic cloves, crushed

a little freshly grated nutmeg

salt and freshly ground black pepper

3 eggs, lightly beaten

low calorie cooking spray

2 x 45g ready-rolled filo pastry sheets, halved

Preheat the oven to 180°C/Fan 160°C/Gas 4.

Cook the spinach according to the packet instructions then tip into a colander. Press out the excess liquid and squeeze dry with kitchen paper or a clean tea towel. Roughly chop and set aside to cool in a large bowl.

Add the spring onions to the spinach along with the parsley, dill, feta, cottage cheese, garlic and nutmeg. Season to taste and mix to combine then pour in the eggs and mix again.

Spray a 30 x 20cm ovenproof dish with low calorie cooking spray and spoon in the spinach mixture. Lightly spray the filo sheets with low calorie cooking spray and scrunch them over the top of the spinach mixture to cover. Bake for 30-35 minutes or until golden and serve warm with your favourite potatoes and salad.

fasolia gigantes

~giant baked beans~

If you love baked beans you'll love this ultimate version! It's packed with filling beans and flavoured with warming cumin and cinnamon.

serves 4

Free

❄ V SP

ready in 1 hour, plus standing

- low calorie cooking spray
- 1 large onion, finely chopped
- 3 garlic cloves, finely chopped
- 4 tbsp tomato purée
- 2 x 400g cans cherry tomatoes
- ¼ tsp ground cumin
- 1 tsp dried oregano
- ¼ tsp ground cinnamon
- small handful of finely chopped fresh parsley
- salt and freshly ground black pepper
- 4 x 400g cans butter beans, drained and rinsed

Preheat the oven to 180°C/Fan 160°C/Gas 4.

Spray a large non-stick frying pan with low calorie cooking spray and place over a medium heat. Add the onion and garlic and cook for 5-6 minutes or until softened.

Add the tomato purée, cherry tomatoes, cumin, oregano, cinnamon and most of the parsley, turn the heat to high and bring to the boil. Reduce the heat to medium, simmer for 3-4 minutes then season to taste and stir in the beans.

Transfer the mixture to a medium-sized ovenproof dish and bake, uncovered, for 40 minutes.

Leave to stand for 5 minutes then scatter over the remaining parsley and serve with your favourite vegetables.

Instead of baking this dish you could cook it over a medium-low hob for 40 minutes.

chickpea salad with griddled halloumi

Halloumi cheese was invented in Cyprus and has become hugely popular all over Greece – and further afield too! This simple salad shows it off at its very best.

serves 4

4 Syns per serving

Ⓥ (if the cheese is vegetarian)

ready in 35 minutes

---

1 aubergine, roughly chopped

1 courgette, roughly chopped

1 red pepper, halved, deseeded and roughly chopped

1 yellow pepper, halved, deseeded and roughly chopped

2 red onions, roughly chopped

low calorie cooking spray

salt and freshly ground black pepper

130g reduced fat halloumi cheese, thickly sliced

400g can chickpeas, drained and rinsed

large handful of roughly chopped fresh coriander

large handful of roughly chopped fresh mint

1 tsp ground cumin

¼ tsp ground cinnamon

juice of 2 lemons

Preheat your oven to 200°C/Fan 180°C/Gas 6.

Put the aubergine, courgette, peppers and onions in a non-stick baking tin, spray with low calorie cooking spray and season. Roast for 20 minutes or until golden and tender, turning and spraying with more low calorie cooking spray halfway through.

Meanwhile, spray a griddle pan with low calorie cooking spray and place over a medium heat. Add the halloumi slices and fry for 5-6 minutes or until lightly golden and nicely charred, turning and spraying with low calorie cooking spray halfway through. Cut the halloumi into chunks or dice and set aside.

Remove the vegetables from the oven and transfer to a mixing bowl. Stir in the chickpeas and fresh herbs.

Mix together the cumin, cinnamon and lemon juice and pour over the salad. Season, toss well and divide between shallow bowls. Scatter over the halloumi to serve.

honey and yogurt cheesecake

serves 10

4 Syns per serving

V

ready in 1 hour 10 minutes, plus cooling and chilling

Greek yogurt and honey are world-famous and play a big part in Greek cuisine. In fact their history of bee-keeping goes back to ancient times… and this amazing cheesecake will definitely create a buzz!

- 4 level tbsp extra-light spread
- 10 light digestive biscuits, finely crushed
- 500g quark
- 250g fat free natural Greek yogurt
- 4 large eggs
- 2 level tbsp honey (Greek if possible)
- 1 tsp ground cinnamon, plus extra to dust
- 2 tsp vanilla essence
- 2 tbsp sweetener
- finely grated zest and segments from 2 oranges
- 200g fat free natural fromage frais, sweetened to taste

Melt the extra-light spread in a pan over a low heat. Add the crushed biscuits and stir to mix well. Spoon into a 22cm non-stick spring-form cake tin, pressing down firmly to make a smooth and even base. Chill until needed.

Preheat the oven to 160°C/Fan 140°C/Gas 3.

Put the quark, yogurt, eggs, honey, cinnamon, vanilla essence, sweetener and orange zest in a large bowl. Beat until well combined and pour over the biscuit base. Bake for 45-50 minutes or until just set and golden. Remove from the oven and leave to cool completely.

Remove the cheesecake from the tin, cover with cling film and chill for 6-8 hours or overnight if possible.

When you're ready to eat, spread the fromage frais over the top of the cheesecake and dust with the extra cinnamon.

Cut into slices and serve with orange segments.

The Middle East and Turkey

This magical melting pot of cultures has created some fabulous spicy food, with filling favourites like falafel and houmous, pilaf and kebabs catching on all over the world. They're sure to be a hit in your home too!

baba ghanoush

-smoky aubergine dip-

serves 4

Free

V

ready in 30 minutes, plus cooling and standing

- 4 aubergines, trimmed
- salt and freshly ground black pepper
- juice of 1 lemon, plus extra to taste
- 2 garlic cloves, crushed
- small handful of finely chopped fresh mint
- small handful of finely chopped fresh parsley
- 100g quark
- 1 tbsp pomegranate seeds
- pinch of smoked paprika, to garnish

The Middle East is home to some of the world's greatest dips and this aromatic and creamy aubergine blend might just be the best of the lot!

Preheat the grill to medium-high.

Put the aubergines in a single layer on the grill pan and grill for 15-20 minutes or until the skins are charred and the aubergines have collapsed a little. Leave to cool then split the aubergines open and scoop out the flesh with a spoon, discarding the skins. Roughly chop the flesh and put it in a colander to drain for 30 minutes. Season to taste.

Meanwhile, mix the lemon juice, garlic and two-thirds of the chopped herbs in a small bowl and season to taste. Check the flavour and add a squeeze more lemon juice if you like.

Put the drained aubergine flesh and quark in a serving bowl. Add the lemon mixture and mix well with a fork. Scatter over the remaining herbs, the pomegranate seeds and the paprika. Serve warm or at room temperature with your favourite vegetable crudités.

For an even smokier flavour, adventurous cooks can blacken the aubergines over a naked flame on a gas hob, turning regularly with tongs until completely charred – this will take about 15-20 minutes (it's a good idea to surround the rings with foil, as things can get messy!). Set aside to cool before scooping out the flesh.

potato, chive and parsnip latkes

serves 4 (makes 20)

½ **Syn** per serving

(V)

ready in 45 minutes

- 400g potatoes
- 400g parsnips
- 4 eggs
- small handful of finely chopped fresh chives, plus extra to garnish
- 1 level tbsp cornflour
- salt and freshly ground black pepper
- low calorie cooking spray
- fat free natural yogurt, to serve

These tasty savoury cakes are much-loved in Israel and are a traditional treat during the Jewish festival of Chanukah. They're fantastic as a starter or side dish.

Preheat the oven to 220°C/Fan 200°C/Gas 7 and line two baking sheets with non-stick baking parchment.

Peel and coarsely grate the potatoes. They will release a lot of starch, so rinse the grated potatoes well in a bowl of cold water. Drain, wrap them in a clean tea towel and squeeze out as much water as you can, then put them in a large bowl.

Peel and coarsely grate the parsnips then add to the potatoes along with the eggs, chives and cornflour. Season and mix well.

Divide the mixture into 20 portions using your hands and arrange the portions on two non-stick baking sheets. Flatten each portion lightly with a spatula, lightly spray with low calorie cooking spray and bake for 15-20 minutes or until golden.

Arrange the latkes on a serving dish, scatter over the extra chives and serve with a bowl of fat free natural yogurt on the side.

tabbouleh

~bulgar wheat and herb salad~

serves 4

Free

Ⓥ

ready in 20 minutes, plus standing

This simple yet sensational salad is all about the herbs so use the freshest leaves you can find. The bulgar wheat will fill you up while the other flavours tantalise your tastebuds.

- 350g dried bulgar wheat
- 6 large tomatoes, finely chopped
- juice of ½ lemon, plus wedges to serve
- large handful of roughly chopped fresh mint
- large handful of roughly chopped fresh parsley
- ¼ tsp ground cumin
- salt and freshly ground black pepper

Cook the bulgar wheat according to the packet instructions. Drain and wrap in a clean tea towel to absorb as much water as possible, then put the bulgar wheat in a large bowl.

Add the tomatoes and all their seeds and juices to the bulgar wheat, stir well and set aside for 30 minutes.

Stir in the lemon juice, herbs, cumin and seasoning and mix well.

Tabbouleh is fantastic served at room temperature with lemon wedges to squeeze over.

falafel and houmous

serves 4 (makes 16 falafel)

Free

V

ready in 50 minutes, plus chilling

Filling chickpeas are the main ingredient in savoury bites known as falafel and the creamy dip, houmous – it's no wonder they go so well together!

for the falafel

low calorie cooking spray

1 onion, finely chopped

2 garlic cloves, crushed

2 x 400g cans chickpeas, drained

2 tsp ground cumin

1 tsp dried mixed herbs

small handful of finely chopped fresh parsley, plus extra to garnish

1 egg, lightly beaten

finely grated zest of 1 unwaxed lemon

salt and freshly ground black pepper

lettuce leaves, to serve

fat free natural yogurt, to serve

pinch of smoked paprika or cayenne pepper, to serve (optional)

for the houmous

400g can chickpeas

1 garlic clove, crushed

2 tbsp lemon juice, plus extra to taste

2 tbsp fat free natural Greek yogurt

pinch of smoked paprika or cayenne pepper, to serve (optional)

Make the falafel first. Spray a non-stick frying pan with low calorie cooking spray and place over a medium heat. Add the onion and stir-fry for 3-4 minutes or until softened. Add the garlic and fry for a further 2 minutes then transfer the mixture to a food processor along with the chickpeas, cumin, mixed herbs, parsley, egg and lemon zest. Season to taste and blend until fairly smooth.

Divide the mixture into 16 equal portions, shape them into balls and spread them out on a non-stick baking tray. Chill for 25-30 minutes.

Preheat the oven to 200°C/Fan 180°C/Gas 6.

Spray the falafel balls with low calorie cooking spray and bake for 25 minutes or until crisp and golden brown. Turn them occasionally to ensure they cook evenly.

Meanwhile, make the houmous. Put the chickpeas, garlic, lemon juice and Greek yogurt into a food processor and pulse until fairly smooth. Season with salt and freshly ground black pepper and add more lemon juice to taste. Transfer to a bowl and sprinkle with the paprika or cayenne pepper if you want an extra kick.

Arrange the falafel on a bed of lettuce leaves, drizzle with the yogurt and sprinkle over the extra parsley and paprika or cayenne pepper, if using. Serve hot or warm with the houmous.

cucumber salad with za'atar

serves 4

½ **Syn** per serving

Ⓥ

ready in 20 minutes

---

4 tomatoes, roughly chopped

1 cucumber, peeled, halved lengthways, deseeded and roughly chopped

1 green pepper, halved, deseeded and roughly chopped

1 red pepper, halved, deseeded and roughly chopped

1 red onion, roughly chopped

small handful of finely chopped fresh parsley

juice of 1 lemon

salt and freshly ground black pepper

a few sprigs of fresh mint, to garnish

for the za'atar

2 tsp dried thyme

2 tsp dried oregano

1 tsp dried marjoram

2 tsp sumac (or use 1 tsp grated unwaxed lemon zest)

1 tsp sesame seeds

1 tsp sea salt

This zingy salad is bursting with freshness and the za'atar mix, made using the tangy Middle Eastern spice sumac, is the icing on the cake!

Put the tomatoes, cucumber, peppers, onion, parsley and lemon juice in a large bowl, season to taste and toss together.

Put all the za'atar ingredients in a small bowl and mix well.

Sprinkle the za'atar over the salad vegetables and garnish with the mint sprigs to serve.

Za'atar is believed to sharpen the mind, and many parents in the Middle East make their children eat bread and za'atar before their exams!

beef köfte
with sumac and yogurt dressing

Köfte kebabs are loved all over the Middle East and beyond. The mix of herbs and spices makes them incredibly more-ish and because they're completely Free you can eat as many as you like!

serves 4

Free

❄ (without the dressing)

ready in 30 minutes

800g lean beef mince (5% fat or less)

2 onions, finely chopped

4 garlic cloves, crushed

large handful of finely chopped fresh parsley, plus roughly chopped parsley to garnish

1 tbsp dried thyme

2 tsp ground cumin

2 tsp ground black pepper

1 tbsp sumac (or use 1 tsp finely grated unwaxed lemon zest), plus extra to garnish

2 eggs

low calorie cooking spray

for the dressing

300g fat free natural Greek yogurt

2 garlic cloves, crushed

salt

1 tsp sumac (or use ½ tsp finely grated unwaxed lemon zest)

Preheat the oven to 200°C/Fan 180°C/Gas 6.

Put the mince in a deep bowl and add the onions, garlic and parsley. Mix well.

Add the dried herbs and spices, break in the eggs and knead the mixture with your fingers until it's very smooth. (The more you knead, the better the taste will be.)

Divide the mixture into eight portions and shape each one into a sausage shape around a metal skewer (or use wooden skewers soaked in water for 20 minutes to stop them burning).

Arrange the skewers in a single layer in a roasting tin lined with non-stick baking parchment. Spray lightly with low calorie cooking spray and roast for 15 minutes or until just cooked through.

Meanwhile, make the dressing by mixing the yogurt and garlic with a little salt. Sprinkle the sumac over the top.

Arrange the köfte on a platter, scatter over the extra parsley and serve hot with the dressing, rice and salad.

hünkar beğendi

~sultan's delight~

serves 4

Free

SP

ready in 2 hours

This tempting lamb stew served on a bed of spiced creamy aubergine is a Turkish favourite. And if it's good enough for a sultan, it's good enough for us!

low calorie cooking spray

500g lean lamb leg steaks, visible fat removed, cut into bite-sized pieces

1 onion, finely chopped

3 garlic cloves, crushed

4 tbsp tomato purée

2 x 400g cans chopped tomatoes

1 tsp dried thyme

1 tsp dried oregano

200ml boiling chicken stock

4 aubergines, trimmed

1 tsp ground cumin

¼ tsp ground cinnamon

juice of 1 lemon

300g quark

salt and freshly ground black pepper

small handful of roughly chopped fresh mint and parsley, to garnish

Spray a large non-stick frying pan with low calorie cooking spray and place over a high heat. Add the lamb and stir-fry for 6-8 minutes or until it's nicely browned.

Turn the heat to low, add the onion and stir-fry for 10-12 minutes. Add the garlic and cook for 1-2 minutes, stirring frequently, then add the tomato purée, chopped tomatoes, dried herbs and stock. Cover the pan and simmer for 1½ hours or until the lamb is tender.

Preheat the grill to medium-hot.

Arrange the aubergines in a single layer on the grill pan and grill for 15-20 minutes or until the skins are charred and the aubergines have collapsed a little. Leave to cool then split the aubergines open and scoop out the flesh with a spoon, discarding the skins. Roughly chop the flesh and transfer to a food processor with the cumin, cinnamon, lemon juice and quark. Season to taste and blend until fairly smooth. Set aside and keep warm.

Divide the aubergine mixture around the sides of four shallow bowls and spoon the lamb stew into the middle. Scatter over the chopped herbs and serve hot with salad.

sucuklu yumurta

~sausage and baked eggs~

serves 4

2 Syns per serving

ready in 40 minutes

Sausages, spices and eggs are a winning combination and this easy dish is a treat for breakfast, lunch or dinner.

---

small bag of baby spinach leaves

low calorie cooking spray

8 Sainsbury's Be Good to Yourself Cumberland Sausages, Less Than 3% Fat*, sliced diagonally

1 tsp sweet smoked paprika

1 tsp sumac (or use ½ tsp grated unwaxed lemon zest)

1 tsp dried chilli flakes

1 onion, finely chopped

2 garlic cloves, crushed

2 tomatoes, roughly chopped

salt and freshly ground black pepper

4 eggs

small handful of finely chopped fresh parsley, to garnish

Put the spinach in a non-stick frying pan with a tablespoon of water and place over a medium-high heat. Cook for 1-2 minutes or until wilted then remove from the pan, squeeze out the excess water and set aside.

Dry the pan with kitchen paper and spray with low calorie cooking spray. Add the sausages to the pan and stir-fry for 5 minutes or until lightly browned. Remove from the pan and set aside with the spinach.

Mix the paprika, sumac and chilli in a small bowl.

Add the onion and garlic to the pan and stir-fry for 5 minutes or until softened. Add the tomatoes and half the spice mix, season to taste and cook for 4 minutes. Remove the pan from the heat.

Return the sausages and spinach to the pan, stir to combine and spread evenly around the pan. Make four indentations into the mixture, crack an egg into each one and sprinkle over the remaining spice mix.

Cover the pan, turn the heat to medium-low and cook for 6-8 minutes or until the eggs are cooked to your liking (you could also finish it off under a medium grill).

Scatter over the parsley and serve hot with a crisp green salad.

**We've counted 1 Syn each for the sausages but Syn values for branded foods can change. You can find the very latest information online at www.slimmingworld.com/lifelineonline.*

For an authentic and delicious twist, add 90g crumbled reduced fat feta cheese for an extra 2 Syns per serving. Add half of the cheese before you crack in the eggs, then the rest just after.

ciğer tava

~liver with onion salad~

serves 4

Free

SP

ready in 20 minutes

1 tsp ground cumin

1 tsp smoked sweet paprika, plus extra to garnish

1 tsp sumac (or use ½ tsp finely grated unwaxed lemon zest)

1 tsp dried chilli flakes

500g calves' liver, trimmed, rinsed and patted dry with kitchen paper

for the onion salad

2 red onions, halved and thinly sliced

4 tomatoes, deseeded and roughly chopped

1 cucumber, halved lengthways, deseeded and thinly sliced

2 Little Gem lettuces, leaves separated

1 garlic clove, crushed

juice of 2 lemons

salt and freshly ground black pepper

Exotic sumac and smoked paprika lend their fabulous flavours to calves' liver in this stunning Turkish salad.

First make the onion salad. Mix the red onions, tomatoes, cucumber and lettuce in a large bowl. Mix the garlic with the lemon juice and pour over the salad. Season and set aside.

Mix the cumin, paprika, sumac and chilli flakes in a shallow bowl. Slice the liver into thick pieces and tip into the spices, stirring to coat well. Season with salt and freshly ground black pepper.

Place a large, non-stick griddle pan or frying pan over a high heat. Add the liver and cook for 2-3 minutes, turning once or until the pieces are browned all over and cooked to your liking (take care not to overcook them or they will become tough).

Divide the salad between plates, top with the liver and scatter over the extra paprika to serve.

You can use lamb or chicken livers instead if you fancy a change.

chicken pilaf

While Italy has risotto and Spain has paella, the Middle East has pilaf – a stunning rice dish packed with aromas and flavours. We've added chicken but you could use any other meat or vegetables you like.

serves 4

Free

ready in 40 minutes

low calorie cooking spray

1 large onion, finely sliced

2 tsp ground cumin

2 tsp ground coriander

1 tsp sumac (or ½ tsp grated unwaxed lemon zest)

1 tsp chilli flakes

350g dried basmati or long-grain rice

salt

850ml boiling chicken stock

4 cooked skinless and boneless chicken breasts, cut into bite-sized chunks

200g trimmed green beans, roughly chopped

small handful of finely chopped fresh parsley

3 tbsp pomegranate seeds

Spray a wide non-stick pan (that has a lid) with low calorie cooking spray and place over a medium-low heat. Add the onion and cook for 8-10 minutes or until softened.

Add all of the spices and cook for 1 minute then stir in the rice, season with salt, pour in the stock and bring to the boil. Cover tightly, turn the heat to low and gently simmer for 10 minutes.

Fold the cooked chicken through the rice and cook for another 5 minutes. Remove from the heat and set aside for 5 minutes, still covered, until the rice is tender and the chicken is piping hot.

Meanwhile, cook the green beans in a small pan of lightly salted boiling water for 4 minutes or until tender. Drain the beans and fold into the pilaf along with the parsley and pomegranate seeds.

Serve hot.

chicken shish kebabs with coleslaw

serves 4

Free

(kebabs only)

ready in 25 minutes

1 tsp dried rosemary, plus extra to garnish

1 garlic clove, crushed

finely grated zest of 1 unwaxed lime

2 tsp ground cumin

salt and freshly ground black pepper

4 skinless and boneless chicken breasts, cut into bite-sized chunks

1 tsp smoked paprika, to garnish

for the coleslaw

1 red cabbage, finely shredded

3 carrots, peeled and coarsely grated

1 small onion, thinly sliced

juice of 2 limes

2 tbsp fat free natural yogurt

1 tsp ground cumin

1 tsp sumac (or use ½ tsp grated unwaxed lime zest)

small handful of finely chopped fresh mint and coriander

It wouldn't be the Middle East without some delicious kebabs, and these come with a colourful coleslaw that's packed with goodness.

Preheat the grill to high.

Mix the rosemary, garlic, lime zest and cumin in a bowl. Season and mix then add the chicken chunks and stir to coat well. Thread the chunks on to eight metal skewers (or wooden skewers that have been soaked in water for 20 minutes to stop them burning).

Grill the kebabs for 10 minutes or until cooked through, turning occasionally.

Meanwhile, mix all the ingredients for the coleslaw in a large bowl.

Sprinkle the kebabs with rosemary and paprika and serve hot with the coleslaw and lots of rice.

Chilli sauce (½ Syn per level tablespoon) will give these juicy kebabs a real kick.

uskumru

~grilled mackerel with spicy potatoes~

serves 4

Free

ready in 45 minutes

1kg potatoes, peeled and cut into bite-sized chunks

low calorie cooking spray

1 onion, halved and sliced

4 tbsp tomato purée

1 tsp dried chilli flakes (or more if you like)

juice of ½ lemon, plus wedges to serve

8 fresh mackerel fillets

salt and freshly ground black pepper

small handful of finely chopped fresh dill or parsley

for the dip

1 tsp mustard powder

100g fat free fromage frais

1 tbsp white wine vinegar

The strong flavour of mackerel is magnificent with sizzling potatoes in this spicy Turkish twist on fish 'n' chips!

Preheat the oven to 220°C/Fan 200°C/Gas 7.

Cook the potatoes in lightly salted boiling water for 8-10 minutes then drain and arrange on a baking tray lined with non-stick baking parchment. Spray with low calorie cooking spray and roast at the top of the oven for 25 minutes or until golden.

Meanwhile, spray a large non-stick frying pan with low calorie cooking spray and place over a low heat. Add the onion and fry for 20-25 minutes or until it starts to soften.

Stir the tomato purée and chilli flakes into the onion and cook for 5 minutes then tip in the potatoes and stir well. Squeeze over the lemon juice.

While the onions are cooking, preheat the grill to high.

Make 3-4 diagonal slashes on each side of the mackerel fillets. Season with salt and pepper, place on the grill pan skin side up and cook for 8-10 minutes or until cooked through (without turning them).

Make the dip by mixing the mustard powder, fromage frais and vinegar in a bowl.

Divide the mackerel and spiced potatoes between plates, scatter over the dill or parsley and serve hot with the dip, lemon wedges and your favourite vegetables.

stuffed aubergines with a creamy dip

serves 4

Free

(without the dip)

ready in 45 minutes

In this eye-catching dish, diced aubergine flesh is tossed with fresh salad veg and served in the shells of the aubergines! Try this as a main course with rice or as a stylish side dish with lamb.

2 large aubergines

2 garlic cloves, finely chopped

bunch of spring onions, finely chopped

2 tsp ground cumin

1 tsp ground coriander

1 tsp ground cinnamon

1 red pepper, halved, deseeded and roughly chopped

2 ripe tomatoes, roughly chopped

salt and freshly ground black pepper

low calorie cooking spray

for the dip

250g fat free natural yogurt

small handful of finely chopped fresh mint, plus torn leaves to garnish

Preheat the oven to 220°C/Fan 200°C/Gas 7.

Slice the aubergines in half lengthways and carefully scoop out the flesh, leaving thick shells. Place the shells cut side up in a non-stick roasting tin and set aside.

Dice the aubergine flesh and put it in a bowl with the garlic, spring onions, spices, red pepper and tomatoes. Season and stir to mix well.

Spoon the mixture back into the aubergine shells, spray with low calorie cooking spray and bake for 25 minutes or until the aubergines are tender.

Meanwhile, make the dip by mixing the yogurt and mint in a bowl. Season to taste.

Scatter the extra mint over the aubergines and dip, and serve with salad and rice, if you like.

pomegranate and orange jellies

serves 4

1½ Syns per serving

ready in 20 minutes, plus cooling and setting

---

4 sheets of leaf gelatine

juice of 1 large orange, plus 1 segmented orange to serve

200ml pomegranate juice

1 tbsp sweetener

½ tsp ground cinnamon

100g pomegranate seeds, to decorate

These exquisite jellies show off the fantastic flavour of the pomegranate, an exotic fruit that has has become popular across the whole Mediterranean.

Put the gelatine sheets in a bowl, cover with cold water and leave to soak for 10 minutes.

Meanwhile, put the orange juice, pomegranate juice, sweetener, cinnamon and 200ml of water in a saucepan over a medium heat. Bring almost to the boil then remove from the heat.

Drain the gelatine sheets and squeeze out the excess liquid. Add the sheets to the hot fruit juice, stir until dissolved and leave to cool.

Pour the mixture into four individual jelly moulds, cover and chill for 6-8 hours or until set.

When you're ready to serve, dip the moulds in hot water for a few seconds and gently turn out on to dessert dishes, using a small palette knife if necessary.

Scatter the pomegranate seeds over the jellies and serve with orange segments.

Most supermarkets sell fresh pomegranate seeds, or you can buy whole pomegranates in larger supermarkets or from your greengrocer and remove the seeds yourself.

coffee and cardamom pots

serves 4

2½ Syns per serving

ready in 15 minutes, plus cooling and setting

Crushed cardamom is widely used in Middle Eastern sweet dishes and the coffee flavour makes these elegant puds a perfect way to round off a meal.

- 3 sheets of leaf gelatine
- 1 tsp finely crushed cardamom seeds
- 500ml hot black filter coffee, plus 4 coffee beans to decorate (optional)
- 4 tbsp light condensed milk
- 1 tbsp sweetener
- 4 tbsp fat free natural fromage frais, sweetened to taste
- 1 level tsp cocoa powder, to decorate

Put the gelatine in a bowl, cover with cold water and leave to soak for 10 minutes.

Meanwhile, put the cardamom, coffee and condensed milk in a small pan over a medium-low heat. Bring almost to the boil, then remove from the heat and stir in the sweetener.

Drain the gelatine sheets and squeeze out the excess liquid. Add the sheets to the hot coffee mixture, stir until dissolved and leave to cool.

Divide the mixture between four coffee cups, cover and chill for 6-8 hours or until set.

When you're ready to serve, top each cup with a tablespoon of fromage frais, decorate with a coffee bean if you like and dust with cocoa powder.

cook's tips

eggs

Pregnant women, the elderly and babies shouldn't eat raw or partially cooked eggs. We'll make a note in any recipes where raw or partially cooked eggs are used.

fat free natural fromage frais and yogurt

These are wonderful ingredients when you're Food Optimising as they give the creamy texture and taste normally achieved with cream. However, they tend to separate when boiled and can make the dish look unappetising. So unless the recipe says otherwise, add yogurt or fromage frais off the heat once all the other ingredients have been cooked and simply heat through. Both make great savoury or sweet ingredients – if you're using them to top a pudding, add sweetener and maybe some vanilla essence as well, to taste.

fresh, canned and frozen

Frozen ingredients and canned veg and beans are great alternatives to fresh foods and are so handy to keep in the cupboard or freezer. They'll keep for much longer, can be quicker to cook and are just as good for you. So feel free to switch between all three – bear in mind cooking times may change slightly.

fresh herbs

These lose their freshness quickly so if you have more than you can use, freeze them in a little water in ice cube trays – then you can add them straight to stews and curries.

fruit

While most fresh whole fruit is Free, puréed or cooked fruit counts as Syns because it isn't as filling and becomes much easier to over-consume. You'll see that in any recipes where fruit is puréed or cooked, we've counted it as Syns.

low calorie cooking spray

To cut down on fat in recipes, we recommend using non-stick cookware/bakeware wherever possible. However, where you do need to use fat then choose a low calorie cooking spray which contains 1 calorie or less per spray, as these are Free – others would need to be counted as Syns. Ideal for fried eggs, roast potatoes and chips!

meat and poultry

Trim off any visible fat before cooking to make lean meat or poultry Free, and remember to remove the skin before or after cooking poultry. If you cook poultry with the skin on, cook it separately from the other ingredients so that the fat can't run into them (eg don't roast potatoes in the same tin).

measurements

Syns for some ingredients are based on level teaspoons or tablespoons. Without measuring carefully, it's easy to far exceed your intended Syn intake without realising – so scrape a knife along the top of the spoon, knocking the excess back into the container. For best results, invest in a set of measuring spoons.

minced meat

Lean minced meat (5% fat or less) is a Free Food. Beef, pork and turkey mince are available in most major supermarkets at 5% fat or less – check the nutrition information to be sure. If possible, drain off any fat that comes from the mince while you're cooking it. No chicken and lamb mince is widely available with 5% fat or less so these would have a Syn value… unless you know a friendly butcher who'll mince skinless chicken breasts or lean lamb with all visible fat removed for you.

mustard powder

Made-up mustard in jars has Syns because it contains Synned ingredients while mustard powder is Free, making it a great choice for dressings and sauces.

seasoning

Where salt and pepper are used, we usually suggest seasoning to taste. Official advice is that adults should eat no more than 6g of salt a day – and bear in mind that small amounts can quickly add up.

stock

Fresh stock, stock cubes, stock pots, bouillon powder, ready-to-use liquid stock and liquid stock concentrate are all Free but be aware that gravy granules or powder and stock granules are not. Stock should normally be boiling when you add it to the pan, as cold stock will slow down cooking times.

symbol sense

ready in…

This gives a guide to how long the recipe will take to prepare and cook.

serves…

This gives you an idea of how many people the recipe can serve. However, feel free to split the recipe between more or fewer people instead, depending on how hungry you are – especially when it's Free!

freezer-friendly ❄

Recipes showing this symbol can be safely frozen for up to 1 month. Keep in mind official advice on freezing safely:

- Label food for the freezer with details of what the meal is and when you cooked it.
- Make sure food has cooled before you put it in the freezer.
- Defrost frozen meals completely and reheat thoroughly before eating.

Batch cooking: Wherever you see the freezer-friendly symbol ❄, you can save time and effort by cooking double or triple amounts and freezing the rest to enjoy at a later date. You'll usually save money too because it's often cheaper to buy ingredients in bulk.

suitable for vegetarians V

Recipes marked with this symbol are suitable for vegetarians. Recipes that contain meat, fish or poultry can often be made vegetarian by using Quorn mince or pieces, textured vegetable protein/soya protein or tofu instead. Some ingredients that are unsuitable for vegetarians might surprise you so always check the packaging to be sure.

Extra Easy SP

For super-charged weight loss, go for dishes marked Extra Easy SP. Ask your Slimming World Consultant for more details.

index

did you know?

10p from the sale of this book goes to our charitable foundation SMILES (Slimmers Making it a Little Easier for Someone), whose charity partners have included the NSPCC, Barnardo's, Cancer Research UK and the Marie Keating Foundation. In 2013 we donated £100,000 from book sales.

Published in 2015 by
Slimming World
Clover Nook Road
Somercotes
Alfreton
Derbyshire
DE55 4SW
UK
www.slimmingworld.com

Created and designed by
Slimming World's publications team.
Publications manager: Allison Brentnall
Editor: Oliver Maxey
Designers: Kathryn Briggs and Fabiana Viracca-Butler

Recipes and food styling: Sunil Vijayakar
Photographs: Lara Holmes
Styling: Morag Farquhar

Front cover photograph:
Moules marinières, page 17

Back cover photographs, from top:
Greek salad with watermelon, page 171
Margherita pizza, page 150
Tagliatelle bolognese, page 137
Mixed paella, page 71

© Slimming World – 2015. All rights reserved. No part of this publication may be reproduced, stored in a retrieval system, or transmitted, in any form, mechanical, electronic, photocopying, recording or otherwise, without the prior written consent of Slimming World.

The Slimming World logo, the words "Slimming World" and other words and symbols used in this book are registered trademarks belonging to Miles-Bramwell Executive Services Limited t/a Slimming World.

Produced in China by Sherwood Press.